1. **a)** Start at 102. Count on by 2. Circle these numbers.

b) Start at 102. Count on by 5. Put an X on each number.

c) Write the numbers that have both an X and are circled.

_____

_____

d) Write the pattern rule for the number pattern.

_____

101	102	103	104	105	106	107	108	109	110
111	112	113	114	115	116	117	118	119	120
121	122	123	124	125	126	127	128	129	130
131	132	133	134	135	136	137	138	139	140
141	142	143	144	145	146	147	148	149	150
151	152	153	154	155	156	157	158	159	160
161	162	163	164	165	166	167	168	169	170
171	172	173	174	175	176	177	178	179	180
181	182	183	184	185	186	187	188	189	190
191	192	193	194	195	196	197	198	199	200

2. Look at the squares with circled numbers in this multiplication chart.

a) Write a pattern rule for the position pattern.

_____

_____

_____

b) Write a pattern rule for the number pattern.

_____

_____

X	1	2	3	4	5	6	7
1	1	2	3	4	5	6	7
2	2	4	6	8	10	12	14
3	3	6	9	12	15	18	21
4	4	8	12	16	20	24	28
5	5	10	15	20	25	30	35
6	6	12	18	24	30	36	42
7	7	14	21	28	35	42	49

Stretch Your Thinking

Follow this position rule. Put an X in the squares on the chart. The squares with an X lie along every third diagonal, starting at the first diagonal. The diagonals go 1 down and 1 right.

1	2	3	4	5	6	7	8	9	10	11	12
13	14	15	16	17	18	19	20	21	22	23	24
25	26	27	28	29	30	31	32	33	34	35	36
37	38	39	40	41	42	43	44	45	46	47	48

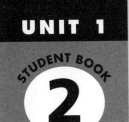

UNIT 1
STUDENT BOOK LESSON 2

Exploring Number Patterns

Quick Review

➤ The first four **terms** are the **core** of this **repeating pattern**.

The core of a pattern is the smallest part that repeats.

2 8 2 9 2 8 2 9 2 8 2 9 ...

➤ In a **growing pattern**, the numbers get bigger in a predictable way.

1   6   11   16   21
Pattern rule: Start at 1. Add 5 each time.

1   3   9   27
Pattern rule: Start at 1. Multiply by 3 each time.

1   2   4   7   11   16   22
Pattern rule: Start at 1. Add 1. Increase the number you add by 1 each time.

➤ In a **shrinking pattern**, the numbers get smaller in a predictable way.

71   66   61   56   51   46
Pattern rule: Start at 71. Subtract 5 each time.

Try These

1. Write the next three terms for each pattern.

   a) 4, 7, 10, 13, _____

   b) 5, 1, 2, 5, 1, 2, 5, 1, 2, _____

   c) 3, 6, 12, 24, _____

   d) 2, 3, 5, 8, 12, _____

   e) 59, 56, 53, 50, _____

1. Write the next four terms for each pattern. Write the pattern rule.

   a) 1, 3, 6, 10, 15, _____

   Rule: _____

   _____

   b) 1, 2, 2, 3, 3, 3, _____

   Rule: _____

   _____

2. Write a repeating pattern. Circle the core.

   _____

3. a) Write the first six terms of a growing pattern using multiplication.

   _____

   b) Write the pattern rule. _____

Stretch Your Thinking

You decide to work out 5 minutes the first day, 6 minutes the second day, 8 minutes the third day, 11 minutes the fourth day, and so on.

a) Record and extend the pattern in the table.

b) On which day will you work out for

   exactly one hour? _____

c) Write the pattern rule.

   _____

   _____

   _____

Day	Time in Minutes
1	
2	
3	
4	
5	
6	
7	
8	
9	
10	
11	

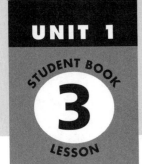
Number Patterns with a Calculator

Quick Review

Explore number patterns with a 4-function calculator.

➤ Count by 8s starting at 15.

Press 15 $\boxed{+}$ 8 $\boxed{=}$ $\boxed{=}$ $\boxed{=}$ …

The pattern is:

15, 23, 31, 39, 47, 55, 63, 71, 79, 87, …

This is a growing pattern.

It has a repeating pattern in the ones digits:

5, 3, 1, 9, 7, 5, 3, 1, 9, 7, …

Its core is 5, 3, 1, 9, 7.

➤ Start at 1. Multiply by 4 repeatedly.

Press 4 $\boxed{\times}$ 1 $\boxed{=}$ $\boxed{=}$ $\boxed{=}$ …

The pattern is: 1, 4, 16, 64, 256, 1024, 4096, …

This is a growing pattern.

It has a repeating pattern in the ones digits:

1, 4, 6, 4, 6, 4, 6, …

Its core is 4, 6.

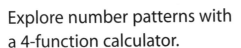

Try These ·

1. **a)** Start with 7. Count by 12s. Record the first ten terms.

_____

b) Record the pattern in the ones digits. Circle its core.

_____

2. **a)** Start with 2. Multiply by 4 repeatedly. Record the first six terms.

_____

b) Record the pattern in the ones digits. Circle its core.

_____

1. Record the next three terms. Write the rule.

   a) 425, 470, 515, 560, 605, 650, _____

   Rule: _____

   b) 742, 712, 682, 652, 622, 592, _____

   Rule: _____

2. **a)** Write a 3-digit number with all the digits the same. _____

   Add the digits of your number. _____

   Divide your 3-digit number by the sum of the digits. _____
   Repeat for three other 3-digit numbers in which
   all the digits are the same.

   _____

   b) What do you notice? _____

3. **a)** Choose any 2-digit number. _____

   Multiply your number by 101. _____
   Repeat with three other 2-digit numbers.

   _____

   b) What do you notice? _____

   _____

Stretch Your Thinking

a) Record the next six terms of this pattern.

   1, 4, 9, 16, 25, 36, _____
b) What pattern rule did you follow?

   _____

   _____

Equations Involving Addition

Quick Review

Here are the addition facts for the number 8.

$0 + 8 = 8$	$5 + 3 = 8$
$1 + 7 = 8$	$6 + 2 = 8$
$2 + 6 = 8$	$7 + 1 = 8$
$3 + 5 = 8$	$8 + 0 = 8$
$4 + 4 = 8$	

Look at the pattern in the numbers that are added.
The first number in each fact increases by 1:
0, 1, 2, 3, …
The second number in each fact decreases by 1:
8, 7, 6, 5, …

An **equation** is a number sentence that shows two things are equal.

An addition fact is an equation.
$9 + 3 = 12$

You can use any pair of addition
facts for a number to make an equation.
$5 + 3 = 4 + 4$

$5 + 3 = 8$ and $4 + 4 = 8$,
so,
$5 + 3 = 4 + 4$

Try These

1. Complete each pattern.

a)
$$0 + 11 = 11$$
$$1 + 10 = 11$$
$$2 + 9 = 11$$

b)
$$15 + 0 = 15$$
$$14 + 1 = 15$$
$$13 + 2 = 15$$

2. Find the missing number in each equation.

a) $8 + \underline{\quad} = 17$ b) $\underline{\quad} + 10 = 21$ c) $12 = \underline{\quad} + 7$ d) $16 = 8 + \underline{\quad}$

1. Find the number that completes each equation. Use counters to help.

   a) $2 + 8 = 4 +$ _____   **b)** $4 + 9 =$ _____ $+ 10$

   c) _____ $+ 5 = 9 + 9$ **d)** $5 +$ _____ $= 3 + 11$

   e) $4 + 11 =$ _____ $+ 3$ **f)** $7 + 6 = 3 +$ _____

2. Find all the ways of making each statement an equation.

   a)

   $7 + 6 =$ _____ $+$ _____

   b)

   $10 + 2 =$ _____ $+$ _____

3. **a)** Find two ways to write 12 as a sum of three numbers.

   _____ $+$ _____ $+$ _____ $= 12$ _____ $+$ _____ $+$ _____ $= 12$

   b) Find two ways to write 17 as a sum of three numbers.

   $17 =$ _____ $+$ _____ $+$ _____ $17 =$ _____ $+$ _____ $+$ _____

Stretch Your Thinking

1. **a)** Jillian has 125 guppies and 40 tetras. Ling has 65 different kinds of fish. How many more fish does Ling need so that he and Jillian have an

   equal number of fish? _____

   b) Write an equation to show your answer. _____

Equations Involving Subtraction

Quick Review

Here are the subtraction facts you can make with 7 counters.

$7 - 7 = 0$	$7 - 3 = 4$	Look at the pattern in the numbers.
$7 - 6 = 1$	$7 - 2 = 5$	The number that is subtracted decreases by 1:
$7 - 5 = 2$	$7 - 1 = 6$	7, 6, 5, 4, 3, 2, 1, 0
$7 - 4 = 3$	$7 - 0 = 7$	The difference increases by 1:
		0, 1, 2, 3, 4, 5, 6, 7

You can use a pair of subtraction facts
to make an equation.
The differences must be the same.
$9 - 4 = 12 - 7$

$9 - 4 = 5$ and $12 - 7 = 5$,
so,
$9 - 4 = 12 - 7$

Try These

1. Complete each pattern.

a)
$13 - 0 = 13$
$13 - 1 = 12$
$13 - 2 = 11$

b)
$11 - 11 = 0$
$11 - 10 = 1$
$11 - 9 = 2$

2. Find the missing number in each equation.

a) $16 - \underline{\quad} = 9$

b) $12 = 20 - \underline{\quad}$

c) $8 = \underline{\quad} - 4$

d) $\underline{\quad} - 10 = 16$

1. Find the number that completes each equation. Use counters to help.

   a) $17 - 9 = 13 - \underline{\hspace{1cm}}$

   b) $15 - 6 = \underline{\hspace{1cm}} - 9$

   c) $13 - \underline{\hspace{1cm}} = 10 - 1$

   d) $\underline{\hspace{1cm}} - 12 = 9 - 2$

   e) $11 - 7 = 16 - \underline{\hspace{1cm}}$

   f) $\underline{\hspace{1cm}} - 5 = 14 - 3$

2. Find four ways of making each statement an equation.

   a)
   $15 - 8 = \underline{\hspace{1cm}} - \underline{\hspace{1cm}}$

   b)
   $17 - 3 = \underline{\hspace{1cm}} - \underline{\hspace{1cm}}$

3. Renée had 14 bunnies and Arden had 12.
   Renée sold 5 bunnies.
   How many bunnies would Arden have to sell so that he and Renée have an

   equal number of bunnies? _____

   Write an equation to show your answer. _____

4. Explain how you know that $22 - 7 = 35 - 20$ is an equation.

   _____

   _____

Stretch Your Thinking

Use each of these numbers once.
Write three equations using subtraction facts.

1	2	3	4
5	6	7	8
9	10	11	12

_____

_____

_____

Whole Numbers to 10 000

At Home
At School

Quick Review

You can show the number 1453 in different ways:

➤ Use Base Ten Blocks.

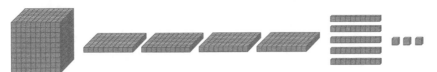

1 thousand   4 hundreds   5 tens   3 ones

➤ Use a place-value chart.

Thousands	Hundreds	Tens	Ones
1	4	5	3

➤ Use **expanded form**. 1453 = 1000 + 400 + 50 + 3
➤ Use words.   1453 = one thousand four hundred fifty-three

The number 1453 is written in **standard form**.
Every digit has a place value, depending on its position.

Try These . . . .

1. Write each number in standard form.

   a) two thousand six hundred thirteen _____

   b) 8000 + 600 + 40 + 1 _____

2. Write each number in expanded form.

   a) 7125 _____   **b)** 2307 _____

3. Write each number in words.

   a) 1620 _____

   b) 3408 _____

Practice

1. Complete the chart.

	Standard Form	Expanded Form
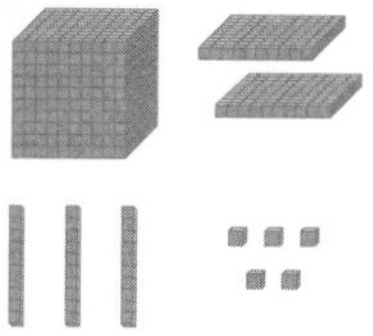		
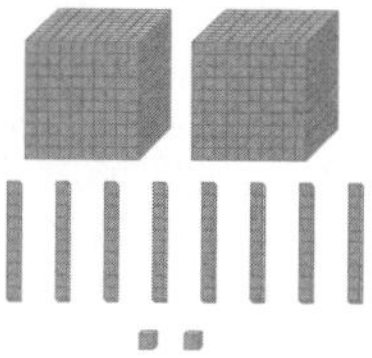		
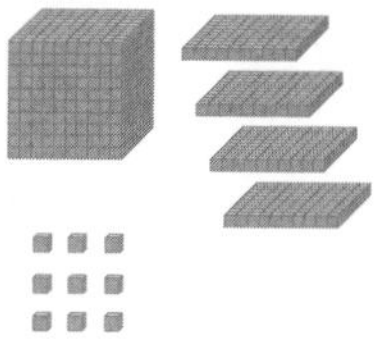		

2. Write each number in words.

   a) 3602 ______________________________

   b) 5045 ______________________________

3. Use each of these digits once to make each 4-digit number: 4, 2, 7, 5

   a) the greatest possible number ________

   b) the least possible number ________

   c) the greatest number with 5 tens ________

   d) the least number with 5 ones ________

Stretch Your Thinking

Use 5, 3, 1, and 7 once in each number you make.
Make as many 4-digit numbers as you can.

____

____

Rounding Numbers

At Home
At School

Quick Review

➤ Round 3482 to the nearest **thousand**.
482 is closer to 0 than to 1000.
So, 3482 rounds to 3000.

3482

3000   3500   4000

➤ Round 3482 to the nearest **hundred**.
Since 82 is closer to 100 than to 0, add 1 hundred.
So, 3482 rounds to 3500.

3482

3400   3450   3500

➤ Round 3482 to the nearest **ten**.
2 is closer to 0 than to 10.
So, 3482 rounds to 3480.

3482

3480   3485   3490

Try These

Use a number line when it helps.

1. Round to the nearest thousand.

    a) 1489 _____   **b)** 6973 _____   **c)** 4215 _____

2. Round to the nearest hundred.

    a) 5867 _____   **b)** 8214 _____   **c)** 7098 _____

3. Round to the nearest ten.

    a) 6281 _____   **b)** 5389 _____   **c)** 2302 _____

Use this table for questions 1 and 2.

Attendence at a Baseball Game

Day	Number of People
Friday	3741
Saturday	4352
Sunday	4837

1. Round each number to the nearest thousand. _____
   On which day did about 5000 people attend the baseball game?

   _____

2. Round each number to the nearest hundred. _____
   On which day did about 4400 people attend the baseball game?

   _____

3. Write three numbers that round to 2540 when rounded to the nearest ten.

   _____

4. Write three numbers that round to 3600 when rounded to the nearest

   hundred. _____

5. Write three numbers that round to 8000 when rounded to the nearest

   thousand. _____

6. A number is rounded to the nearest ten, nearest hundred, and nearest
   thousand. All the rounded numbers are 8000. What was the number

   before it was rounded? _____

Stretch Your Thinking . . . .

How many numbers less than 1000 would round to 1000 when rounded
to the nearest hundred? Explain.

_____

_____

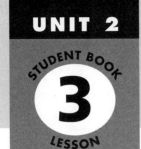

Comparing and Ordering Numbers

Quick Review

Here are some ways to order the numbers 3261, 3621, and 2163 from least to greatest.

➤ Use a place-value chart.

Thousands	Hundreds	Tens	Ones
3	2	6	1
3	6	2	1
2	1	6	3

2163 has the fewest thousands, so it is the least number.

Both 3261 and 3621 have 3 thousands. Compare their hundreds.
200 < 600
So, 3261 < 3621

< means less than.
> means greater than.

➤ Use a number line.

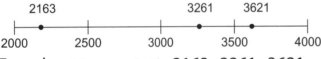

From least to greatest: 2163, 3261, 3621

Try These . . . .

1. Compare each pair of numbers. Write >, <, or =.

    a) 627 ☐ 485   b) 2641 ☐ 4824   c) 2683 ☐ 2683

2. Write the numbers in order from least to greatest.

    758, 709, 741 _____

3. Write the numbers in order from greatest to least.

    7148, 6271, 7285 _____

1. Play this game with a partner.
   The object of the game is to make the greater number.
   You will need a paper bag containing 10 cards with the digits 0 to 9.

   ➤ Draw a card from the bag.
      Record the digit in any space in the first row of your game board.
      Return the card to the bag.
   ➤ Take turns until each player fills all four spaces in a row.
   ➤ Compare your numbers.
      Write > or < in the box between the numbers.
      The player with the greater number wins a point.
   ➤ Play two more rounds.
      The player with the most points at the end of the game wins.

Player 1		Player 2
___ ___ ___ ___	☐	___ ___ ___ ___
___ ___ ___ ___	☐	___ ___ ___ ___
___ ___ ___ ___	☐	___ ___ ___ ___

2. a) Put your numbers from the game in order from least to greatest.

      _____

   b) Put your partner's numbers in order from greatest to least.

      _____

Stretch Your Thinking

Make up three 4-digit numbers.
Order the numbers from greatest to least.

_____

Estimating Sums

Quick Review

When a question asks "about how many," you can estimate.

Here are some ways to estimate the sum of 294 + 351.

➤ Use **rounding**.
Round each number to the nearest 100 and add.
300 + 400 = 700
So, 294 + 351 is about 700.

➤ Use **clustering**.
Both 294 and 351 are about 300.
300 + 300 = 600
So, 294 + 351 is about 600.

➤ Use **front-end estimation**.
Add the first digits of the numbers.
200 + 300 = 500
So, 294 + 351 is about 500.

For a better estimate:
Think about 94 and 51.
This is about 100 + 50 = 150.
So, 294 + 351 is about 500 + 150 = 650.

Try These . . . .

1. Estimate each sum.
   a) 198 + 389

   Estimate: _____

   b) 119 + 408

   Estimate: _____

   c) 640 + 192

   Estimate: _____

   d) 79 + 272

   Estimate: _____

   e) 516 + 482

   Estimate: _____

   f) 291 + 291

   Estimate: _____

2. William estimated 246 + 585 as 700. Is his estimate high or low? Explain.

   _____

   _____

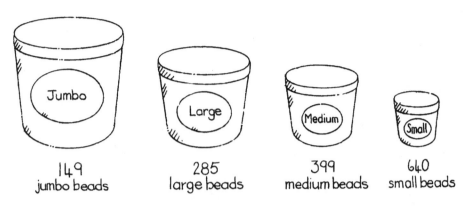

149
jumbo beads

285
large beads

399
medium beads

640
small beads

1. About how many beads would you have if you bought these sizes:

    a) small and large? _____   **b)** medium and jumbo? _____

    c) medium and large? _____   **d)** jumbo and small? _____

2. The toy shop sold 117 wind-up cars and 289 battery-operated cars
    in one week. About how many cars did it sell? _____

3. Yolanda has a desktop publishing business. She wants to print
    1000 items today. She actually prints 352 brochures and 581 flyers today.

    a) About how many items did she print? _____

    b) Did Yolanda make her goal? Explain.

    _____

    _____

4. Last summer, 227 children signed up for T-ball and 139 signed up for
    baseball. About how many children signed up altogether? _____

Stretch Your Thinking

The estimated sum of two numbers is 1000.
What might the numbers be? Give three different answers.

_____

Using Mental Math to Add

At Home
At School

Quick Review

➤ Use mental math to add: 267 + 197
Use the strategy of "make a friendly number."
197 is 200 − 3.
Add 200, then take away 3.
267 + 200 = 467
467 − 3 = 464
So, 267 + 197 = 464

> 200 is a friendly number because it is easy to add 200.

➤ Use mental math to add: 271 + 580
Make a "friendly" number.
580 + 20 = 600
271 − 20 = 251
So, 271 + 580 = 600 + 251 = 851

> 600 is a friendly number.

➤ Use mental math to add: 415 + 342
Use the strategy of "adding on."
Add on hundreds, then tens, and then ones.
Think: 415 + 300 + 40 + 2
Count on 3 hundreds: 415, 515, 615, 715
Count on 4 tens: 715, 725, 735, 745, 755
Then add 2: 755 + 2 = 757
So, 415 + 342 = 757

Try These . . . .

1. Use mental math to add.

   a) 262 + 345 = _____   b) 497 + 222 = _____   c) 370 + 163 = _____

   d) 399 + 544 = _____   e) 262 + 290 = _____   f) 196 + 341 = _____

2. Becky gathered 316 clams and Charlie gathered 286.

   How many clams did they gather in all? Use mental math to find out. _____

Use mental math.

1. Add.

   a) 690 + 284 = _____

   b) 131 + 468 = _____

   c) 352 + 213 = _____

   d) 229 + 493 = _____

   For which problems did you make a "friendly" number? _____

2. Look at these containers.
   If you bought the following groups
   of animals, how many toy animals
   would you have?

   a) farm animals and zoo animals _____

   b) sea creatures and jungle animals _____

   c) zoo animals and jungle animals _____

3. Ridgetown has a population of 317 people.
   Mayberry has a population of 291.

   How many people live in the two towns? _____

4. The cafeteria sold 123 cartons of chocolate milk and 204 cartons of

   white milk. How many cartons of milk were sold? _____

Stretch Your Thinking

Use mental math to add: 453 + 197 + 205 = _____

Describe the strategy you used. _____

_____

_____

_____

_____

Adding 3-Digit Numbers

At Home
At School

Quick Review

Geraldo has 276 hockey cards and 397 baseball cards.
To find how many cards Geraldo has in all, add: 276 + 397

Here are some ways to add:

➤ Use expanded form.

$$276 \longrightarrow 200 + 70 + 6$$
$$+\,397 \longrightarrow 300 + 90 + 7$$
$$500 + 160 + 13 = 660 + 13 = 673$$

➤ Use place value.

Add the ones: 13 ones	Add the tens: 17 tens	Add the hundreds:
Regroup 13 ones as	Regroup 17 tens as	6 hundreds
1 ten and 3 ones.	1 hundred and 7 tens.	

$$\begin{array}{r} \overset{1}{2}7\mathbf{6} \\ +\,39\mathbf{7} \\ \hline \mathbf{3} \end{array} \qquad \begin{array}{r} \overset{1\ 1}{2}7\mathbf{6} \\ +\,39\mathbf{7} \\ \hline \mathbf{7}\mathbf{3} \end{array} \qquad \begin{array}{r} \overset{1\ 1}{2}7\mathbf{6} \\ +\,39\mathbf{7} \\ \hline \mathbf{6}73 \end{array}$$

Geraldo has 673 cards in all.

Try These

1. Add.

a) 295
+ 104

b) 327
+ 415

c) 299
+ 463

d) 508
+ 419

e) 285
+ 79

2. There were 139 more people at the soccer game on Saturday than on Friday.
On Friday there were 472 people at the game.

How many people were at the game on Saturday? _____

1. Estimate first.
   Circle the letters next to the examples for which
   the sum will be less than 900.
   Then, add to find all the sums.

   a)   738   b)   637   c)   109   d)   718   e)   367
       + 191   + 439   + 488   + 237   + 662

   f)   482   g)   234   h)   689   i)   651   j)   318
       + 519   + 410   + 130   + 259   + 491

2. Estimate first.
   Circle the letters next to the examples for which
   the sum will be greater than 700.
   Then, add to find all the sums.

   a)   418   b)   526   c)   381   d)   108   e)   397
       + 231   + 437   + 294   + 592   + 459

   f)   362   g)   583   h)   435   i)   339   j)   282
       + 282   + 199   + 428   + 382   + 531

3. Use expanded form to add. Show your work.

   a)   352   b)   453
       + 539   + 372

4. What is the greatest number you can add to 457 without having to

   regroup in any place? _____

Stretch Your Thinking
. . . .

The sum of two numbers is 853. What might the numbers be?

Find two pairs of numbers. _____

Adding 4-Digit Numbers

At Home
At School

Quick Review

Add: 1756 + 2469

➤ Use expanded form to add.

$$1756 \longrightarrow 1000 + 700 + 50 + 6$$
$$+ 2469 \longrightarrow 2000 + 400 + 60 + 9$$
$$3000 + 1100 + 110 + 15$$

$$4100 + 125 = 4225$$

➤ Use place value to add.

Add the ones.	Add the tens.	Add the hundreds.	Add the thousands.
Regroup.	Regroup.	Regroup.	
1	1 1	1 1 1	1 1 1
1756	1756	1756	1756
+ 2469	+ 2469	+ 2469	+ 2469
5	**25**	**225**	**4225**

Estimate to check that the sum is reasonable.

1756 rounds to 2000.   4225 rounds to 4000.

2469 rounds to 2000.   So, the sum is reasonable.

2000 + 2000 = 4000

Try These

1. Find each sum. Estimate to check.

a)   5558
    + 1343

b)   3047
    + 2828

c)   4189
    + 3673

d)   1847
    + 5684

2. Estimate each sum.

a) 3276 + 4192

Estimate: _____

b) 1258 + 3769

Estimate: _____

c) 2672 + 3409

Estimate: _____

1. Play this game with a partner.
   You will need:
   1 number cube

   ➤ Take turns rolling the number cube.
   On each roll, both players record the digit rolled
   in one of the boxes in their first addition grid.
   ➤ After 8 rolls, players add.
   The player with the greater sum wins.
   ➤ Repeat with the other addition grids.

Player A	Player B

Stretch Your Thinking

The sum of two 4-digit numbers is 4589.
What might the two numbers be?
Give two different answers.

Estimating Differences

Quick Review

Here are some strategies for estimating differences.

➤ Estimate: 513 – 289
Round each number
to the nearest 100
and subtract.
500 – 300 = 200
So, 513 – 289 is about 200.

> To get a better estimate,
> round only one number.
> 513 – 300 = 213.
> So, 513 – 289 is about 213.

➤ Estimate: 592 – 69
One number has only 2 digits,
so round to the nearest 10
and subtract.
590 – 70 = 520
So, 592 – 69 is about 520.

> To get a better estimate,
> round only the number you subtract.
> 592 – 70 = 522.
> So, 592 – 69 is about 522.

Try These

1. Use rounding to estimate each difference.

   a) 749 – 263

   Estimate: _____

   b) 504 – 327

   Estimate: _____

   c) 988 – 214

   Estimate: _____

   d) 580 – 235

   Estimate: _____

   e) 677 – 48

   Estimate: _____

   f) 896 – 58

   Estimate: _____

2. Natalie estimated 584 – 126 as 400. Is her estimate high or low? Explain.

   _____

   _____

   _____

   _____

School Lunches Served

Day	Number Served
Monday	286
Tuesday	327
Wednesday	489
Thursday	417
Friday	648

1. Use the data in the chart to estimate each difference.
   a) About how many more lunches were served on Friday

   than on Monday? _____

   b) About how many more lunches were served on Thursday

   than on Tuesday? _____

   c) About how many more lunches were served on Wednesday

   than on Tuesday? _____

2. Laleh estimated the difference of 765 and 411 as 400, and Sam
   estimated the difference as of 365.
   a) How might Laleh have estimated?

   _____

   _____

   b) How might Sam have estimated?

   _____

   _____

   c) Whose estimate is better? Explain.

   _____

   _____

   _____

Stretch Your Thinking . . . .

Find a pair of 3-digit numbers that have an estimated difference of 520.

_____

UNIT 2

Using Mental Math to Subtract

Quick Review

Here are some strategies for using mental math to subtract.

➤ Use the strategy of "make a friendly number."

Subtract: 719 – 398

Add 2 to 398 to make 400.

Add 2 to 719 to make 721.

721 – 400 = 321

So, 719 – 398 = 321

Subtract: 437 – 103

Subtract 100 instead of 103.

437 – 100 = 337

Then subtract 3.

337 – 3 = 334

So, 437 – 103 = 334

➤ Use the strategy of "counting on."

Subtract: 441 – 230

Count: 230   330   430   440   441

+100   +100   +10   +1   =   211

So, 441 – 230 = 211

Try These

1. Use mental math to subtract.

   a) 427 – 299 = _____ b) 625 – 495 = _____ c) 586 – 397 = _____

   d) 256 – 101 = _____ e) 748 – 403 = _____ f) 462 – 202 = _____

   g) 272 – 150 = _____ h) 758 – 547 = _____ I) 894 – 673 = _____

2. Laslo travelled 637 km on Saturday and 402 km on Sunday.
   How much further did he travel on Saturday than on Sunday?

   Use mental math to find out. _____

3. The hot dog stand served 250 hot dogs on Friday and 481 on Saturday.
   How many more hot dogs were served on Saturday than on Friday?

   Use mental math to find out. _____

1. Use mental math to find each difference.
   Then use the letters next to the differences to solve the riddle.

What did King Tut say when he was scared?

543 – 260 = _____ (B)   622 – 415 = _____ (E)

894 – 517 = _____ (N)   583 – 298 = _____ (I)

499 – 354 = _____ (M)   314 – 189 = _____ (U)

532 – 220 = _____ (T)   847 – 606 = _____ (Y)

684 – 302 = _____ (W)   717 – 402 = _____ (Z)

536 – 199 = _____ (C)   632 – 421 = _____ (F)

947 – 624 = _____ (L)   231 – 111 = _____ (A)

285   382   120   377   312   145   241   145   125   145   145   241

Stretch Your Thinking

Describe two ways to find 1000 – 894.

_____

_____

_____

_____

Subtracting 3-Digit Numbers

At Home
At School

Quick Review

There are 300 seats in the theatre. One hundred eighty-four seats are on the main floor. The rest are in the balcony.

To find how many seats are in the balcony, subtract: 300 – 184

➤ You can use place value to subtract.

You cannot take 4 ones from 0 ones.	Subtract the ones.
There are no tens to regroup.	Subtract the tens.
Regroup 1 hundred as 10 tens.	Subtract the hundreds.
Regroup 1 ten as 10 ones.	

$$
\begin{array}{r}
\overset{9}{2\,\cancel{10}\,10} \\
\cancel{300} \\
-\ 184 \\
\hline
\end{array}
\qquad\qquad
\begin{array}{r}
\overset{9}{2\,\cancel{10}\,10} \\
\cancel{300} \\
-\ 184 \\
\hline
116
\end{array}
$$

➤ You can use mental math to subtract.

Count on from 184 to 300.

$$184 \nearrow 284 \nearrow 294 \nearrow 300$$

$$+100 \qquad +10 \qquad +6 \ =\ 116$$

You can check by adding.

Add: $184 + 116 = 300$

Try These

1. Subtract.

   a) 465
      -213

   b) 786
      -229

   c) 574
      -197

   d) 600
      -211

   e) 238
      $-\ 79$

2. Find the difference. Use mental math.

   a) $400 - 174 = \underline{\hspace{1cm}}$

   b) $500 - 189 = \underline{\hspace{1cm}}$

   c) $347 - 215 = \underline{\hspace{1cm}}$

   d) $701 - 500 = \underline{\hspace{1cm}}$

   e) $428 - 299 = \underline{\hspace{1cm}}$

   f) $152 - 107 = \underline{\hspace{1cm}}$

1. Subtract. Check your answers.

   a)   836
       – 451   Check:

   b)   726
       – 538   Check:

   c)   736
       – 528   Check:

2. Use mental math to find each difference.

   a) 400 – 263 = _____   b) 501 – 248 = _____   c) 450 – 231 = _____

3. Estimate first. Then subtract the numbers for which the difference will be less than 300.

   a)   591   b)   436   c)   624   d)   716   e)   327
       – 375   – 168   – 235   – 371   – 79

4. Ms. Green's class collected 600 cans for recycling.
   Mr. Hso's class collected 427 cans.

   How many more cans did Ms. Green's class collect? _____

5. Sanil's school had a book sale.
   On Monday they sold 697 books.
   On Tuesday they sold 842 books.

   How many more books did they sell on Tuesday? _____

Stretch Your Thinking . . . .

The difference of two numbers is 329.
What might the numbers be? Find two pairs of numbers.

_____

Subtracting from a 4-Digit Number

Quick Review

Subtract: 2053 − 997
Use place value.

Regroup 1 ten as 10 ones. Subtract the ones.	Regroup 1 thousand as 10 hundreds. Regroup 1 hundred as 10 tens.	Subtract the tens. Subtract the hundreds. Subtract the thousands.

$$\begin{array}{r} {\scriptstyle 4\ 13} \\ 205\!\!\!/3 \\ -\ 997 \\ \hline \mathbf{6} \end{array}$$

$$\begin{array}{r} {\scriptstyle 9\ 14} \\ {\scriptstyle 1\ \not{10}\ \not{4}\ 13} \\ \cancel{2053} \\ -\ 997 \\ \hline 6 \end{array}$$

$$\begin{array}{r} {\scriptstyle 9\ 14} \\ {\scriptstyle 1\ \not{10}\ \not{4}\ 13} \\ \cancel{2053} \\ -\ 997 \\ \hline 1056 \end{array}$$

Check.

➤ By adding:
$$\begin{array}{r} 997 \\ +\ 1056 \\ \hline 2053 \end{array}$$

The sum should be the number you started with.

➤ By estimating:
2000 − 1000 = 1000
1000 is close to 1056.
So, the answer is reasonable.

Try These

1. Subtract.
   a) 4532
      − 121

   b) 5726
      − 248

   c) 7243
      − 685

   d) 4029
      − 388

2. Subtract. Check your answer.
   a) 9354
      − 287   Check:

   b) 7600
      − 452   Check:

1. Estimate. Then subtract.

   a) 3059
      − 298

   b) 5138
      − 479

   c) 8209
      − 919

   d) 5439
      − 216

   Estimate: _____   Estimate: _____   Estimate: _____   Estimate: _____

2. Manjit and Irene like to collect acorns.
   Manjit collected 1286 acorns and Irene collected 898.

   How many more acorns did Manjit collect than Irene? _____

3. Play this game with a partner.

   You will need:
   1 number cube
   Paper
   Pencils

   ➤ Each player draws a subtraction grid like this:

   ➤ Take turns rolling the number cube.
      After each turn, both players record the digit
      rolled in any box in their grid.
   ➤ After 7 rolls, players subtract.
      The player with the greater difference wins.
   Play 5 or more games.

   Stretch Your Thinking . . . .

A 3-digit number is subtracted from a 4-digit number.
The difference is 426. What could the two numbers be? Give two answers.

_____

_____

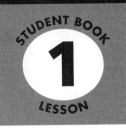

Congruent Figures

Quick Review

Figures that are **congruent** are the same size and shape.

➤ The figures in each pair are congruent.

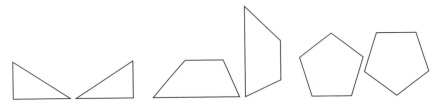

Sometimes, you have to flip or turn a figure to check if it is congruent to another figure.

➤ Tracing paper can help you find out if two figures are congruent.
  • Trace one of the figures.
  • Place the tracing on top of the other figure.
  The figures are congruent if they match.

Try These

1. **a)** Find 3 pairs of congruent figures.
      Join each pair with a line.
      Use tracing paper to check.

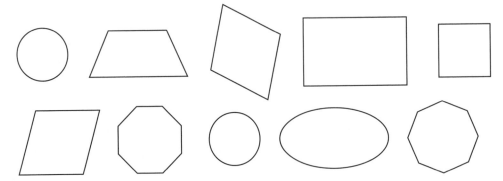

   b) How do you know the figures are congruent?

1. Circle the figure that is congruent to A.

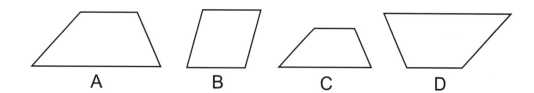

2. Join the dots to divide the figure into
   a) 5 congruent squares   **b)** 2 congruent triangles

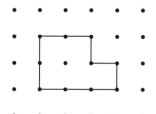
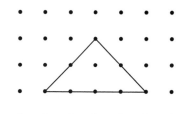

3. Use the dot paper to draw 2 congruent figures.

Stretch Your Thinking ·

Find a different way to divide each square into 4 congruent parts.

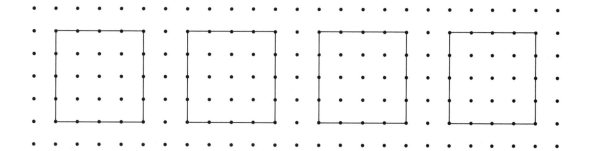

Exploring Angles

Quick Review

An angle is formed when 2 lines cross.

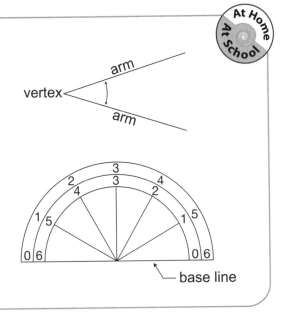

A **protractor** measures angles.

This protractor has units from 0 to 6 clockwise and counterclockwise.

To measure an angle, count how many units fit the angle.

Try These

1. Look at this Pattern Block.
   What can you tell about the 3 angles?

   _____

   _____

2. Write whether each angle is *a right angle, less than a right angle*, or *greater than a right angle*.

Use the 6-unit protractor your teacher gave you.

1. Measure each angle.

a)

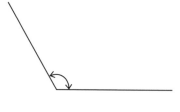

_____

b)

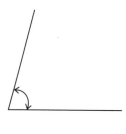

_____

c)

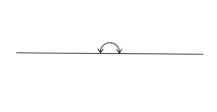

_____

d)

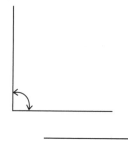

_____

2. Use a ruler. Draw 3 angles. Measure each angle and record your measurements.

_____   _____   _____

Stretch Your Thinking ··

Explain how you can use your protractor to measure this angle.

_____

_____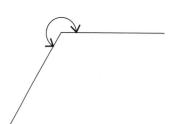

_____

_____

_____

Measuring Angles

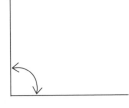
At Home
At School

Quick Review

This is a **standard protractor**.
The standard protractor shows
angle measures from 0° to 180°,
both clockwise and counterclockwise.

Follow these steps to measure
an angle with a protractor.

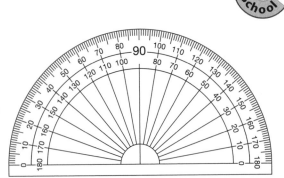

Step 1

Place the protractor on top of the angle.
Line up the centre of the protractor
with the vertex of the angle.
Line up the base line of
the protractor with one
arm of the angle.

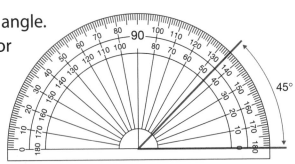

45°

Step 2

Find where the other arm of the angle meets the protractor.
Start at 0° on the arm along the base line and read the measure.
This angle measures 45°.

Try These . . . .

1. Use a protractor to measure each angle. Record the measurements.

   a)

   b)

   c)

   _____   _____   _____

1. Measure each angle. Record the measurements in the chart.

a)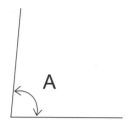

b)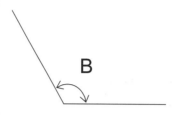

Angle	Measure
A	
B	
C	
D	

c)

d)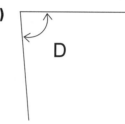

2. Use the angle measures from Question 1. Write <, >, or =.

a) B ☐ C   b) A ☐ D   c) A ☐ B

3. Use a ruler. Estimate to draw each angle.

a) a right angle   b) a 45° angle   c) a 120° angle

4. Measure each angle you just drew. Record the actual measures.

a) _____   b) _____   c) _____

Stretch Your Thinking

1. How many of each kind of angle can you find in this picture? Mark each kind in a different colour.

a) 90° _____

b) greater than 90° _____

c) less than 90° _____

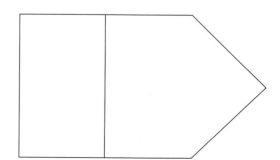

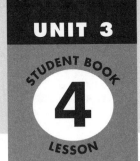
Exploring Sides in Quadrilaterals

Quick Review

At Home At School

A figure with 4 sides is a **quadrilateral**.

➤ Some quadrilaterals have 2 pairs of opposite sides that are equal.

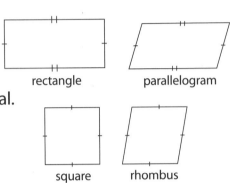

rectangle   parallelogram

A square is a rectangle with 4 sides equal.
A rhombus is a parallelogram with
4 sides equal.
Hatch marks show equal sides.

square   rhombus

➤ Some quadrilaterals have 2 pairs of parallel sides. We draw arrows on lines to show parallel sides.

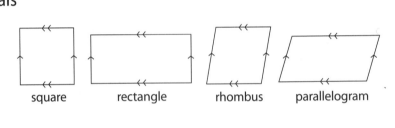

square   rectangle   rhombus   parallelogram

➤ Trapezoids have 1 pair of parallel sides.

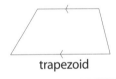

trapezoid

Try These

1. Draw 2 different quadrilaterals on the dot paper.
   Mark equal sides with hatch marks. Mark parallel sides with arrows.

1. Play this game with a partner.

   You will need:
   Dot paper
   Pencil

   Does it have
   equal angles?
   yes

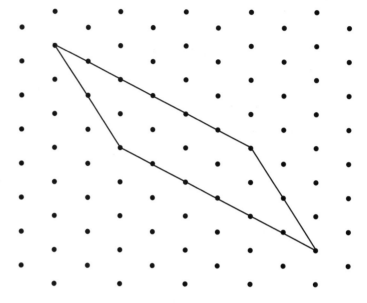

   Player A
   ➤ Make a quadrilateral on the dot paper without letting your partner see.
   The quadrilateral should have at least one pair of equal or parallel sides.

   Player B
   ➤ Ask your partner "Yes–No" questions about the quadrilateral.
   The questions can be about
   • the number of equal sides
   • the number of parallel sides
   • the diagonals
   ➤ Keep asking questions until you think you know the quadrilateral.
   Guess the quadrilateral. If you are right, you get a point.
   Switch roles and play again.
   Keep playing until one player has 5 points.

Stretch Your Thinking

Explain why this quadrilateral cannot be called
a square, a parallelogram, a rectangle,
a rhombus, or a trapezoid.

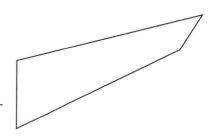

_____

_____

Exploring Angles in Quadrilaterals

At Home
At School

Quick Review

Squares and rectangles have
4 equal angles.
Each angle is 90°.

Parallelograms and rhombuses
have opposite angles equal.

Kites have 2 equal angles.

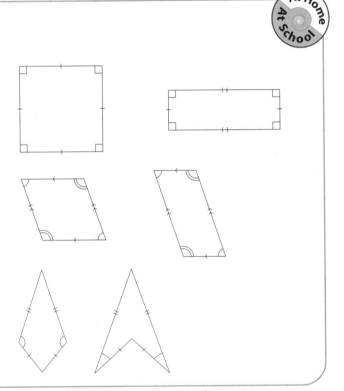

Try These

1. Draw a quadrilateral with each attribute.

   a) 4 right angles   **b)** 2 pairs of equal angles   **c)** only 2 right angles

2. Why is a rectangle not a kite?

_____

_____

1. Use the Venn diagram to sort the quadrilaterals.

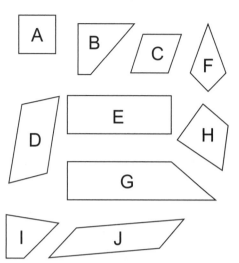

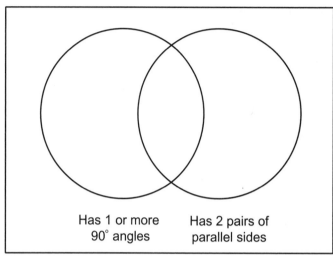

Has 1 or more   Has 2 pairs of
90° angles   parallel sides

2. a) Draw a trapezoid on the dot grid.
   b) Write a statement about
      your trapezoid that is true.

   _____

   _____

   c) Write a statement about a trapezoid
      that is never true.

   _____

   _____

Stretch Your Thinking

Explain why a square is a parallelogram and a rhombus.

_____

_____

_____

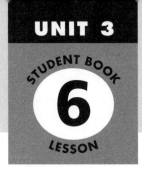
Attributes of Quadrilaterals

Quick Review

At Home
At School

Quadrilaterals	Attributes
Trapezoid	1 pair of parallel sides
Parallelogram	2 pairs of parallel sides opposite sides equal opposite angles equal
Rectangle	2 pairs of parallel sides opposite sides equal all right angles
Square	2 pairs of parallel sides all sides equal all right angles
Rhombus	all sides equal opposite angles equal 2 pairs of parallel sides
Kite	2 pairs of equal adjacent sides 1 pair of equal angles

Try These

1. **a)** How are the figures alike?

   _____

   _____

   _____

   A

   b) How are they different?

   _____

   _____

   B

1. Draw a parallelogram to fit each description.

   a) 4 right angles and 4 equal sides

   b) 2 pairs of parallel sides and no right angles

   c) 4 right angles and 2 pairs of equal sides

2. Solve each quadrilateral riddle. There can be more than one answer for each riddle. Can you find all the answers?

   a) I have 1 pair of equal angles.
   I have 2 pairs of equal adjacent sides.

   What am I? _____

   b) I have 2 pairs of parallel sides.
   All of my sides are equal.
   I have no right angles.

   What am I? _____

   c) I have at least 1 pair of parallel sides.
   I have no right angles.

   What am I? _____

Stretch Your Thinking

Jerry said that since a square is a rectangle, then a rectangle must be a square. What would you say to convince Jerry he is not correct?

_____

_____

Similar Figures

Quick Review

Similar figures have the same shape.
These figures are similar.
They have the same shape.

Each side of Figure B is 2 times the length of a corresponding side of Figure A.

Each angle in Figure B is equal to a corresponding angle in Figure A.

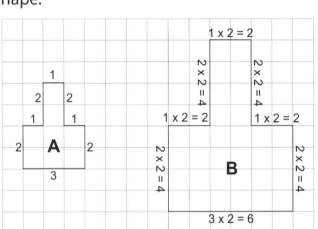

Try These

1. Tell if each pair of figures is similar. Write Yes or No.

   a)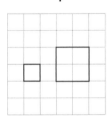

   b)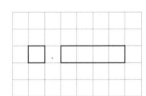

   c)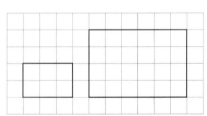

   _____   _____   _____

2. Find pairs of similar figures. Join each pair with a line.

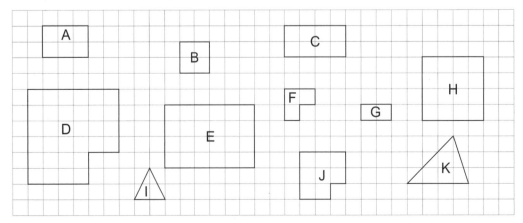

1. Do this activity with a partner.
   ➤ Choose any figure on the grid.
   ➤ Work together to find a figure that is similar.
   ➤ Once you agree, label each with a letter.
   ➤ Continue to find pairs of similar figures.
   ➤ Label each pair with a different letter.

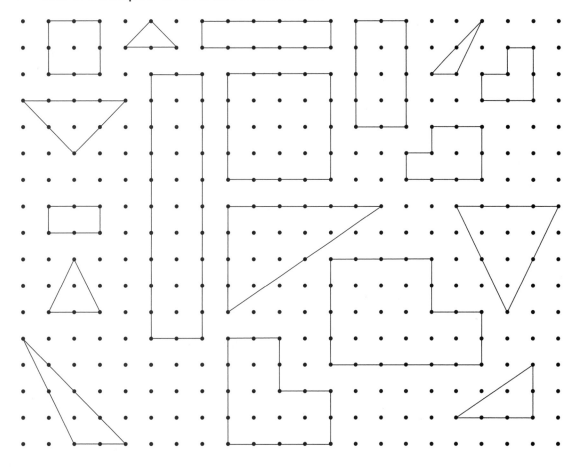

Stretch Your Thinking

Make an *H* and *I* similar to the *H* and *I* on the grid.

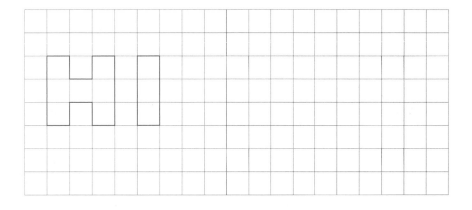

Faces of Solids

At Home
At School

Quick Review

Each surface on a solid is called a **face**.
The base of the figure determines the figure's name.

Solid		Faces
	Rectangular prism	3 pairs of congruent rectangles
	Rectangular pyramid	1 rectangle 2 pairs of congruent triangles
	Cube	6 congruent squares
	Triangular pyramid	4 congruent triangles
	Triangular prism	2 congruent triangles 3 congruent rectangles

Try These

1. Name each solid.

   a) 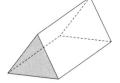   b) 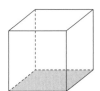   c)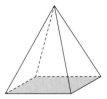

   _____   _____   _____

2. Identify the shape of the shaded face of each solid in question 1.

   a) _____   b) _____   c) _____

1. Identify the solid that has each set of faces.
   a)

   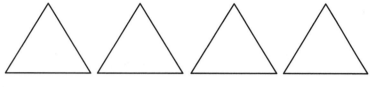

   _____

   b)

   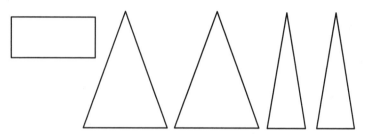

   _____

2. Explain how you identified the solids from the sets of faces in question 1.

   a) _____

   b) _____

   _____

3. Name 3 solids that have triangular faces.
   Tell how many triangular faces each one has.

   a) _____

   b) _____

   c) _____

Stretch Your Thinking

Compare a hexagonal prism and a hexagonal pyramid.
How are they alike? How are they different?

_____

_____

_____

Solids in Our World

Quick Review

You can sort solids in different ways.

➤ You can sort by the number of faces, edges, or vertices.

Has 6 vertices

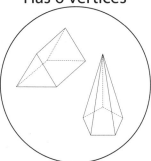

➤ You can sort by the shapes of the faces.

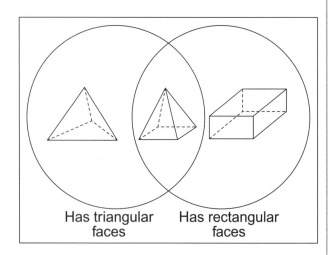

Has 8 vertices

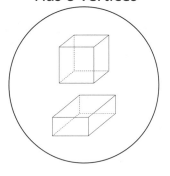

Has triangular faces   Has rectangular faces

Try These

1. Sort the solids.

A
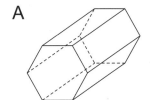

B
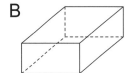

C

D
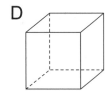

E
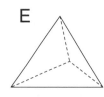

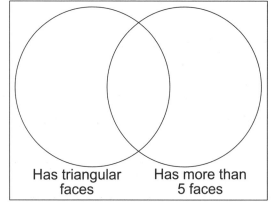

Has triangular faces   Has more than 5 faces

1. Name the solid that best represents each object.

a)

b)

c)

_____ _____ _____

2. Write the names of one or more solids to answer each riddle.

a) My 6 faces are rectangular. _____

b) I have 8 vertices. _____

c) I have 2 circular faces. _____

3. Look through old magazines or catalogues for 3 small pictures of objects that look like solids. Cut them out and paste them here. Name the solid each object resembles.

_____ _____ _____

Stretch Your Thinking . . . .

How can you use the shape of the base of a pyramid to determine the number of faces on the pyramid? Give an example to support your answer.

_____

_____

Designing Skeletons

At Home
At School

Quick Review

A **skeleton** is a model of a solid showing only the edges and vertices. You describe a skeleton by its number of vertices and equal edges.

Skeleton	Number of Vertices	Types of Edges
Cube	8	12 equal edges
Triangular prism	6	3 pairs of equal edges on the triangular bases 3 equal edges joining the bases

Try These

1. This skeleton is made of straws and balls of Plasticine.
   a) How many straws does the

   skeleton have? _____

   b) How many balls of Plasticine

   does the skeleton have? _____

   c) Which solid is the skeleton
   a model of?

   _____

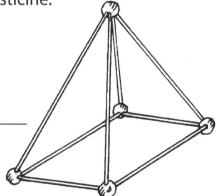

2. How many straws and balls of Plasticine would you need to build a triangular prism?

   straws _____ balls of Plasticine _____

1. Use straws or toothpicks and balls of Plasticine.
    Make skeletons of 2 prisms and 2 pyramids.
    At least 2 skeletons should have some triangular faces.
    Sketch and name the skeletons in the boxes below.

2. Tell how many straws and balls of Plasticine you would need to make
    each skeleton.

Skeleton	Straws	Balls of Plasticine
Cube		
Rectangular pyramid		
Pentagonal pyramid		
Rectangular prism		
Pentagonal prism		

Stretch Your Thinking . . . .

1. Suppose you built a pyramid with an octagonal base.

    a) How many straws would you need? _____

    b) How many balls of Plasticine would you need? _____

    c) How many straws would you need if you used whole straws for the side

       edges and quarter straws for the base edges? _____

UNIT 4

STUDENT BOOK 1 LESSON

Skip Counting

At Home At School

Quick Review

Look at the circled numbers in this multiplication chart.

You say these numbers when you start at 7 and count on by 7s.

These numbers are **multiples** of 7.

Multiplication Chart

X	1	2	3	4	5	6	7	8	9	10
1	1	2	3	4	5	6	7	8	9	10
2	2	4	6	8	10	12	14	16	18	20
3	3	6	9	12	15	18	21	24	27	30
4	4	8	12	16	20	24	28	32	36	40
5	5	10	15	20	25	30	35	40	45	50
6	6	12	18	24	30	36	42	48	54	60
7	7	14	21	28	35	42	49	56	63	70
8	8	16	24	32	40	48	56	64	72	80
9	9	18	27	36	45	54	63	72	81	90
10	10	20	30	40	50	60	70	80	90	100

Try These

1. Use the multiplication chart above.

a) Start at 3. List the multiples of 3. ______________________

b) Start at 6. List the multiples of 6. ______________________

c) Compare the numbers in the lists. What patterns do you see?

____

____

2. **a)** List all the multiples of 2 to 20. ______________________

b) List all the multiples of 4 to 20. ______________________

c) Describe the numbers that are on both lists.

____

____

1. a) Use the hundred chart.
Colour all the numbers in
which the ones digit and
the tens digit add up to 9.

b) What multiples have
you coloured?

_____

_____

_____

Hundred Chart

1	2	3	4	5	6	7	8	9	10
11	12	13	14	15	16	17	18	19	20
21	22	23	24	25	26	27	28	29	30
31	32	33	34	35	36	37	38	39	40
41	42	43	44	45	46	47	48	49	50
51	52	53	54	55	56	57	58	59	60
61	62	63	64	65	66	67	68	69	70
71	72	73	74	75	76	77	78	79	80
81	82	83	84	85	86	87	88	89	90
91	92	93	94	95	96	97	98	99	100

2. Play this game with 2 or 3 friends.

You will need:
2 sets of cards numbered 2 to 10
3 counters for each player
A small container

➤ Take 3 counters each.
➤ Shuffle the cards and put them in a pile face down.
➤ Turn over the top card. This is the number you will start with.
➤ Go around the group. Say one number each, counting on by the number
on the card.
The player who says 100 or a number over 100 puts a counter in the
container.
The next player turns over a new card and starts the counting.
➤ The first person to get rid of all 3 counters wins.

Stretch Your Thinking

1. a) In the game above, which start numbers will result in a player saying 100?

_____

b) Which start numbers will result in a player going over 100?

_____

Multiplying by Numbers to 9

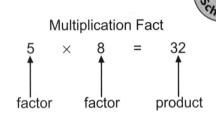

Quick Review

Multiply **factors** in a **multiplication fact** to get a **product**.

Multiplication Fact

$$5 \quad \times \quad 8 \quad = \quad 32$$

factor   factor   product

Here are some ways to help you remember multiplication facts.

Symmetry	Use the diagonal line from 0 to 81 on the multiplication chart. **If 7 × 8 = 56, then 8 × 7 = 56**
Facts with 0	The product is 0 when you multiply by 0. **0 × 7 = 0** **9 × 0 = 0**
Facts with 1	When you multiply by 1, the product is the other factor. **1 × 4 = 4** **6 × 1 = 6**

Facts with 9	• The digits in the product always add up to 9.
	     2 × 9 = 18 (1 + 8 = 9) **3 × 9 = 27 (2 + 7 = 9)**
	
	 • The number multiplied by 9 is always 1 more than the tens digit in the product.
	     6 × 9 = 54 (6 is 1 more than 5.)

Try These

1. Multiply.

    a) 9 × 7 = _____

    b) 6 × 4 = _____

    c) 7 × 6 = _____

    d) 8 × 5 = _____

    e) 0 × 8 = _____

    f) 1 × 9 = _____

    g) 8 × 2 = _____

    h) 8 × 9 = _____

    i) 6 × 5 = _____

    j) 5 × 7 = _____

    k) 6 × 3 = _____

    l) 4 × 8 = _____

1. Play this game with a partner.

You will need:
25 counters
2 calculators
paper and pencils

➤ Decide on a number from 2 to 9. This number will be the game factor.
➤ Player A: Place a counter on any number on the board and multiply by the game factor. Record the product as your score.
➤ Player B: Place a counter on a number adjacent to Player A's number. Multiply by the game factor and record your score.

> When something is *adjacent* to something else, it is next to it.

➤ Continue playing. On each turn, place a counter next to the last one played.
If an adjacent square is not empty, place the counter in any empty square.
➤ When the board is filled, the winner is the player with the highest total score.

1	7	8	4	2
5	8	3	6	4
0	3	4	7	1
2	7	2	9	5
9	1	6	3	0

Stretch Your Thinking . . . .

Suppose you are Player A. Where will you place the first counter? Explain.

_____

_____

UNIT 4

Other Strategies for Multiplying

Quick Review

Use these strategies to multiply.

➤ Use **doubling** to multiply by 4. Multiply by 2, then double.
To find 4×7:
$2 \times 7 = 14$
$14 + 14 = 28$
So, $4 \times 7 = 28$

➤ Use **known facts** to multiply by 6.
To find 6×9:
$5 \times 9 = 45$
$1 \times 9 = 9$
$45 + 9 = 54$
So, $6 \times 9 = 54$

➤ Use **facts with 5 and 2** to multiply by 7.
To find 7×6:
$5 \times 6 = 30$
$2 \times 6 = 12$
$30 + 12 = 42$
So, $7 \times 6 = 42$

Try These

1. Write a multiplication fact for each array.

a) ○○○○○○
○○○○○○
○○○○○○

_____

b) ○○○○○
○○○○○
○○○○○
○○○○○

_____

c) ○○○○
○○○○
○○○○

_____

2. Make an array to find each product.

a) $7 \times 6 =$ _____

b) $8 \times 3 =$ _____

c) $3 \times 9 =$ _____

1. Name two facts that help you find each product.

    a) 7×9 _____

    b) 7×6 _____

    c) 6×8 _____

    d) 6×9 _____

    e) 4×8 _____

    f) 4×7 _____

2. Show how you could find the product of 8×6 if you know the product of 8×5.

_____

3. Play this game with a partner.

    You will need:
    3 number cubes
    2 calculators

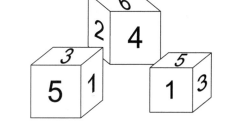

    ➤ Take turns to roll all 3 number cubes.
       Put the one with the greatest number aside.
       If you roll more than one greatest number, put only one aside.
       Roll the other 2 number cubes.
       Put the one with the greater number aside.
       Roll the last number cube.
    ➤ Add the numbers on your first 2 cubes.
       Multiply the total by the number on your third cube.
       The product is your score.
    ➤ Keep playing until one player reaches a total of 200.

Stretch Your Thinking ·

Show how you could use doubling to find the product of 13×4.

_____

Exploring Multiplication Patterns

Quick Review

➤ Use place value to multiply by 10, by 100, and by 1000.
You know $5 \times 1 = 5$.

So, 5×1 ten = 5 tens $5 \times 10 = 50$
5×1 hundred = 5 hundreds $5 \times 100 = 500$
5×1 thousand = 5 thousands $5 \times 1000 = 5000$

➤ Use basic multiplication facts and place value to multiply by
multiples of 10, 100, and 1000.
You know $3 \times 3 = 9$.

So, 3×3 tens = 9 tens $3 \times 30 = 90$
3×3 hundreds = 9 hundreds $3 \times 300 = 900$
3×3 thousands = 9 thousands $3 \times 3000 = 9000$

Try These

Multiply. Use Base Ten Blocks when they help.

1. a) $6 \times 1 =$ _____   b) $8 \times 1 =$ _____   c) $9 \times 1 =$ _____

   $6 \times 10 =$ _____ $8 \times 10 =$ _____ $9 \times 10 =$ _____

   $6 \times 100 =$ _____ $8 \times 100 =$ _____ $9 \times 100 =$ _____

   $6 \times 1000 =$ _____ $8 \times 1000 =$ _____ $9 \times 1000 =$ _____

2. a) $3 \times 2 =$ _____   b) $5 \times 2 =$ _____   c) $4 \times 2 =$ _____

   $3 \times 20 =$ _____ $5 \times 20 =$ _____ $4 \times 20 =$ _____

   $3 \times 200 =$ _____ $5 \times 200 =$ _____ $4 \times 200 =$ _____

   $3 \times 2000 =$ _____ $5 \times 2000 =$ _____ $4 \times 2000 =$ _____

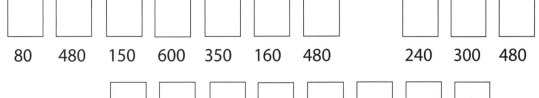

Practice

Find each product. Then fill in the boxes below with the letters that match the products. The words in the boxes will answer this riddle:

Why do rabbits make good mathematicians?

A $6 \times 100 = $ _____

B $8 \times 10 = $ _____

C $3 \times 50 = $ _____

D $80 \times 7 = $ _____

E $6 \times 80 = $ _____

F $3 \times 3000 = $ _____

G $6 \times 400 = $ _____

H $5 \times 60 = $ _____

I $7 \times 100 = $ _____

J $200 \times 5 = $ _____

K $5 \times 100 = $ _____

L $4 \times 30 = $ _____

M $9 \times 10 = $ _____

N $2 \times 9 = $ _____

O $2 \times 1000 = $ _____

P $6 \times 30 = $ _____

Q $7 \times 700 = $ _____

R $3 \times 1000 = $ _____

S $8 \times 20 = $ _____

T $3 \times 80 = $ _____

U $7 \times 50 = $ _____

V $5 \times 1000 = $ _____

W $7 \times 300 = $ _____

X $8 \times 90 = $ _____

Y 4×200 _____

Z $9 \times 50 = $ _____

□ □ □ □ □ □ □   □ □ □ □

80 480 150 600 350 160 480   240 300 480 800

□ □ □ □ □ □ □ □

90 350 120 240 700 180 120 800

Stretch Your Thinking

There are 40 quarters in a roll.
How many quarters are there in 10 rolls?

_____

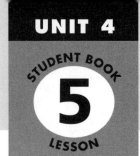
Estimating Products

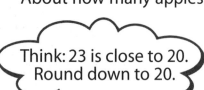
Quick Review

Estimate to solve multiplication problems.

➤ A basket holds 23 apples.
About how many apples do 5 baskets hold?

Think: 23 is close to 20.
Round down to 20.

To estimate 5×23
$5 \times 20 = 100$
There are about 100 apples
in 5 baskets.

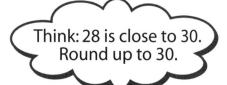
23 apples

➤ A bucket holds 28 tennis balls.
About how many tennis balls do 7 buckets hold?

Think: 28 is close to 30.
Round up to 30.

To estimate 7×28
$7 \times 30 = 210$
There are about 210 tennis balls
in 7 buckets.

Try These

1. Estimate each product.
   a) 4×29 b) 6×52 c) 5×81
      Estimate: _____   Estimate: _____   Estimate: _____

2. There are 48 crayons in a box.

   About how many crayons are there in 8 boxes? _____

3. There are 9 chairs in each row.

   About how many chairs are there in 18 rows? _____

4. Kara bought 27 packs of stickers. There are 8 stickers in each pack.

   About how many stickers does Kara have? _____

1. Estimate each product.

   a) 6×78 _____

   b) 4×93 _____

   c) 9×42 _____

   d) 5×69 _____

   e) 7×21 _____

   f) 52×7 _____

   g) 38×8 _____

   h) 47×6 _____

   i) 84×5 _____

2. About how many gel pens would you
   have if you bought:

   a) 3 boxes? _____

   b) 7 boxes? _____

   c) 5 boxes? _____

   d) 8 boxes? _____

3. Bertha types 58 words a minute.
   About how many words can she type in:

   a) 5 minutes? _____

   b) 8 minutes? _____

   c) 30 minutes? _____

4. Estimate how many treats you would get from:

   a) 6 piñatas _____

   b) 4 piñatas _____

   c) 9 piñatas _____

Stretch Your Thinking . . . .

Jack collects superhero trading cards.
He has 5 collections with 22 cards each and 7 collections with 27 cards each.
About how many cards does Jack have altogether?

_____

Strategies for Multiplication

Quick Review

At Home
At School

Here are three ways to find the product of 5×22.

➤ Use Base Ten Blocks. Arrange 5 groups of 22.

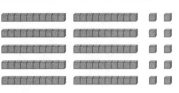

Multiply the tens. $5 \times 20 = 100$
Multiply the ones. $5 \times 2 = 10$
Add. $100 + 10 = 110$

➤ Show an array on grid paper.

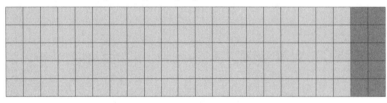

5 rows of $20 = 100$
5 rows of $2 = 10$
Add. $100 + 10 = 110$

➤ Break a number apart.

$$\begin{array}{r} 22 \\ \times\ 5 \\ \hline \end{array}$$

Multiply the ones: $5 \times 2 \ \rightarrow \quad 10$
Multiply the tens: $5 \times 20 \rightarrow \ \underline{100}$
Add. $\qquad\qquad\qquad\quad 110$

Try These

· ·

Write a multiplication sentence.

1. a)

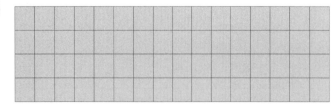

b)

_____   _____

1. Multiply.

   a)   32
        ×4

   b)   42
        ×4

   c)   84
        ×2

   d)   71
        ×8

   e)   65
        ×3

   f)   56
        ×3

   g)   19
        ×5

   h)   57
        ×6

   i)   48
        ×4

   j)   56
        ×9

2. Play this game with a partner.

   You will need:
   10 small pieces of paper with one of these numbers
   written on each piece: 0, 1, 2, 3, 4, 5, 6, 7, 8, 9
   A small paper bag
   Paper and pencil

   ➤ Draw a game space like this on your paper.
   ➤ Put the numbered pieces of paper in a bag.
   ➤ Pull out 3 numbered pieces each.
   ➤ Record each digit in one of the boxes in your game space.
   ➤ Find your products.
     The player with the greater product wins a point.
   ➤ Play 5 rounds.
   ➤ Then, change the rules to make a new game. Record your digits in the
     boxes of your partner's game space. Play 5 more rounds.

Stretch Your Thinking

The box to the right represents the game you just played.
The digit boxes are represented by A, B, and C.
Which digit box is the best place to write your highest number?
Explain.

_____

_____

Dividing by Numbers from 1 to 7

Quick Review

There are 42 students who want to play hockey.
There are 6 players on a team.
How many teams can there be?

To find out, divide: $42 \div 6$
Here are two ways to find $42 \div 6$:

➤ Make an array of 42 counters with
6 counters in each row.
There are 7 rows.
So: $42 \div 6 = 7$
There can be 7 teams.

➤ You can think about
multiplication to divide.
Every division fact has
a related multiplication fact.

 Think:

6 times which
number is 42?
You know $6 \times 7 = 42$
So, $42 \div 6 = 7$

Try These

1. Write a multiplication fact and a division fact for each array.

   a)

   The multiplication is 30

   b)

   The multipliction is 28

2. Use a related multiplication fact to help you divide. Write the related fact.

   a) $20 \div 4 =$ _____

   b) $30 \div 5 =$ _____

   c) $14 \div 7 =$ _____

   _____   _____   _____

1. Divide. Draw a picture to show your work.

$24 \div 3 =$ _____	$30 \div 5 =$ _____
$18 \div 2 =$ _____	$5 \div 5 =$ _____

2. Use a related multiplication fact to divide.

   a) $18 \div 6 =$ _____ b) $45 \div 5 =$ _____ c) $56 \div 7 =$ _____ d) $35 \div 5 =$ _____

   c) $24 \div 4 =$ _____ f) $27 \div 3 =$ _____ g) $12 \div 2 =$ _____ h) $9 \div 1 =$ _____

3. Write a division fact to solve each question.

   a) 24 children   b) 18 cookies   c) 42 cans
      6 on a team   9 on a plate   7 in each row
      How many teams?   How many plates?   How many rows?

   _____   _____   _____

Stretch Your Thinking

Find all the ways of dividing 36 students into equal teams.
Write a division fact to show each way.

_____

_____

_____

_____

Dividing by Numbers from 1 to 9

Quick Review

At Home At School

Here's how to divide by 8 and 9.

48 ÷ 8

8 × ☐ = 48

8 × 6 = 48

So, 48 ÷ 8 = 6

Also, 48 ÷ 6 = 8

Think multiplication.

Related Facts
48 ÷ 8 = 6
48 ÷ 6 = 8
6 × 8 = 48
8 × 6 = 48

63 ÷ 9

9 × ☐ = 63

9 × 7 = 63

So, 63 ÷ 9 = 7

Also, 63 ÷ 7 = 9

Think multiplication.

Related Facts
63 ÷ 9 = 7
63 ÷ 7 = 9
7 × 9 = 63
9 × 7 = 63

Try These

1. Write two multiplication facts and two division facts for each array.

   a) ○○○○○○○○ _____
   ○○○○○○○○
   ○○○○○○○○ _____
   ○○○○○○○○
   ○○○○○○○○ _____
   _____

   b) ○○○○ _____
   ○○○○
   ○○○○ _____
   ○○○○
   ○○○○ _____
   ○○○○
   ○○○○ _____
   ○○○○
   ○○○○

2. Divide.

   a) 27 ÷ 9 = _____   b) 16 ÷ 8 = _____

   c) 45 ÷ 9 = _____   d) 64 ÷ 8 = _____

   e) 36 ÷ 9 = _____   f) 32 ÷ 8 = _____

1. Find the product. Then write a related multiplication fact and two related division facts.

   a) $3 \times 9 =$ _____

   b) $8 \times 5 =$ _____

   c) $9 \times 7 =$ _____

   _____

   _____

   _____

   _____

   _____

   _____

   _____

   _____

   _____

2. Divide.

   a) $49 \div 7 =$ _____

   b) $81 \div 9 =$ _____

   c) $45 \div 5 =$ _____

   d) $27 \div 3 =$ _____

   e) $56 \div 8 =$ _____

   f) $36 \div 6 =$ _____

3. Write a division sentence to show each answer.

   a) There are 28 days in February. How many weeks is that?

   _____

   b) There are 3 tennis balls in a carton.
   How many cartons are needed for 27 balls?

   _____

   c) There are 54 students in the band. They march in 6 equal rows.
   How many students are in each row?

   _____

   d) There are 9 kiwi fruit in a small basket.
   A box contains 72 kiwi fruit in a single layer.
   How many small baskets of kiwi fruit can be made from a box?

   _____

Stretch Your Thinking

Complete this division sentence in as many ways as you can. $\boxed{} \div \boxed{} = 8$

_____

_____

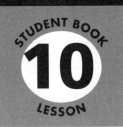

Division with Remainders

Quick Review

➤ Here's how to share 17 pears equally among 5 boxes.

Divide: 17 ÷ 5

Put 3 pears in each box.
There are 2 pears left over.
Write 17 ÷ 5 = 3 R2.
This is a division sentence.
The R stands for remainder.

Say 17 divided by 5
is 3 remainder 2.

➤ Here's how to decide how many tables are needed for 32 students eating in the lunchroom. Six students can fit at each table.
Divide: 32 ÷ 6
Think about the division fact that is closest to 32 ÷ 6.
You know that 30 ÷ 6 = 5. So, 32 ÷ 6 = 5 R2
But if 5 tables are used, then 2 students cannot sit at a table.
So, 6 tables are needed.

Try These

1. Write a division sentence for this picture.

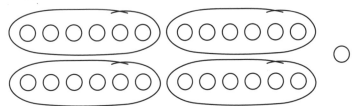

_____

2. Divide.

a) 15 ÷ 6 = _____   b) 27 ÷ 5 = _____   c) 31 ÷ 4 = _____

d) 19 ÷ 6 = _____   e) 17 ÷ 4 = _____   f) 37 ÷ 8 = _____

1. Play this game with a partner.

   You will need:
   Counters of two colours
   Number cubes: one labelled 1, 1, 2, 2, 3, 3 and one labelled 4, 4, 5, 5, 6, 6

   Take turns:
   ➤ Roll the number cubes to make a 2-digit number.
     (For example, with 6 and 3, you can make 63 or 36.)
   ➤ Place a counter on a circled number.
     Divide your 2-digit number by the number in your circle.
   ➤ Place a counter on a square containing your remainder if you can.
   ➤ Remove your counter from the circle.
     Continue playing until all the squares are covered.

7	5	2	4	1
6	3	6	8	6
1	5	0	3	0
2	4	8	7	2
0	5	3	1	4

② ⑥
③ ⑦
④ ⑧
⑤ ⑨

Stretch Your Thinking

1. Write a division sentence with remainder 8.

   _____

2. Write a division sentence with remainder 4.

   _____

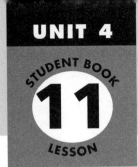
Using Base Ten Blocks to Divide

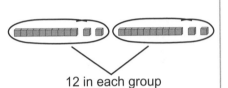
At Home At School

Quick Review

➤ Divide: $24 \div 2$

Divide the blocks into two equal groups.
So, $24 \div 2 = 12$

12 in each group

➤ Divide: $63 \div 5$

There are 10 in each group and 13 left over.

Trade the rod for 10 unit cubes.

Divide the 13 unit cubes among the 5 equal groups.

So, $63 \div 5 = 12$ R3

Try These

Use Base Ten Blocks when they help.

1. Divide.

   a) $88 \div 4 = $ _____

   b) $54 \div 3 = $ _____

   c) $37 \div 2 = $ _____

   d) $89 \div 8 = $ _____

   e) $25 \div 2 = $ _____

   f) $41 \div 3 = $ _____

2. Divide. Draw a picture to show how you got the answer.

$27 \div 7 = $ _____

Practice

1. Divide. Use Base Ten Blocks when they help.

   a) 56 ÷ 7 = _____   b) 81 ÷ 9 = _____   c) 35 ÷ 4 = _____

   d) 27 ÷ 6 = _____   e) 75 ÷ 8 = _____   f) 24 ÷ 6 = _____

2. Write a division sentence to show each answer.
   a) Nine children want to share 36 stickers equally.
      How many will each child get?

   _____

   b) It takes 2 cups of milk to make a milkshake.
      How many milkshakes can be made with 17 cups of milk?

   _____

   c) Emilio is putting 7 treats into each party bag.
      How many bags can he fill with 59 treats?

   _____

3. Three tennis balls fit into each carton.
   How many cartons are needed for 29 tennis balls?

   _____

4. Four children can fit into each seat on the carnival ride.
   How many seats are needed for 39 children?

   _____

5. Write 2 division sentences with remainders.

   _____

Stretch Your Thinking

Daniella divided a number between 45 and 50 by 5. The remainder was 4.
What number did Daniella divide? Write the division sentence.

_____

Another Strategy for Division

Quick Review

Divide: 55 ÷ 2

Arrange the 5 rods in 2 equal rows.

One ten rod and 5 ones remain.

Trade the ten rod for 10 ones.

Now you have 15 unit cubes.

Share the 15 cubes equally among the 2 groups.

So, 55 ÷ 2 = 27 R1

You write:

$$2\overline{)5\,{}^{1}5}$$
$$2$$

$$2\overline{)5\,{}^{1}5}$$
$$2\,7\ R1$$

This is called **short division.**

Try These

1. Divide. Use Base Ten Blocks when they help.

   a) 25 ÷ 8 = _____   **b)** 42 ÷ 5 = _____   **c)** 59 ÷ 7 = _____

   d) 29 ÷ 4 = _____   **e)** 37 ÷ 9 = _____   **f)** 34 ÷ 6 = _____

2. Luis divided 43 marbles equally among his 6 friends. How many marbles did each friend get? Did Luis have any marbles left? Write a division sentence to show how you got the answer.

1. Play this game with a partner.

Start	40	21	33	11	44	29
45						13
49						36
35						15
24						42
19						28
50						32
41	31	20	25	39	48	38

You will need:
1 marker per player
50 counters per player
1 number cube marked 2 to 7

➤ Place your markers on Start.

➤ Take turns.

➤ Roll the number cube. Move that many spaces in either direction.

➤ Divide the number you land on by the number you rolled.
If you have a remainder, give that many counters to your partner.

➤ Continue to take turns. On each turn, you may move your marker in either direction.

➤ Play until one player runs out of counters. That player is the winner.

Stretch Your Thinking

Describe the strategy you used to try to win this game

_____

_____

_____

Reading Data in Tables

Quick Review

This table shows the number of sign-outs and renewals for some popular library books in Lottie's school this year.

Title	Author	Number of Sign-outs	Number of Renewals
Tales of a Fourth Grade Nothing	J. Blume	49	7
512 Ants on Sullivan Street	C. Losi and M. Burns	32	8
Harry Potter and the Order of the Phoenix	J.K. Rowling	63	6
Superfudge	J. Blume	27	0
The Outsiders	S.E. Hinton	56	9

Harry Potter and the Order of the Phoenix was signed out most often.
Superfudge was signed out least often.
The Outsiders was renewed most often.
Superfudge was never renewed.

One fourth of the students who signed out *512 Ants on Sullivan Street* renewed the book. $\frac{1}{4}$ of $32 = 8$

Try These

This table shows the number of books read by some children in one year.

1. Who read the most books? _____

2. How many more books did Cindy read than Yael? _____

3. Who read the fewest books? _____

Name	Number of Books Read
Cam	35
Yael	41
Cindy	57
Ami	59
Terri-Ann	38

1. Use the data in the table to answer the questions.
   a) Which animal sleeps the most hours in a day?

   Ferret, and Squirrel.

   b) Which animal sleeps the least?

   Ferret, Squirrel.

   c) How many more hours does
      a lion sleep than a cow?

      _____

   d) How many hours in a day is
      an African elephant awake?

      _____

   **How Long Animals
   Sleep in a Day**

Animal	Hours
African elephant	3
Brown bat	20
Chimpanzee	10
Cow	4
Ferret	15
Lion	14
Squirrel	15

   e) Which animals spend more than one half of the day sleeping?

   _____

2. Write two questions about the data in this table. Answer your questions.

   **How Long Animals Can
   Hold Their Breath**

Animal	Minutes
Manatee	20
Humpback whale	30
Otter	5
Sea lion	20
Polar bear	2

   a) _____

   _____

   _____

   b) _____

   _____

   _____

Which animals in the table above can hold their breath for $\frac{1}{4}$ hour or more?

_____

Reading Pictographs and Bar Graphs

Quick Review

The **title** of a graph tells you what the graph is about.
The **labels** on the **axes** tell you what data are shown in the graph.

Tickets Sold for Each Performance of the Fourth Grade Play

Tuesday	
Wednesday	
Thursday	
Friday	
Saturday	

☐ = 10 tickets

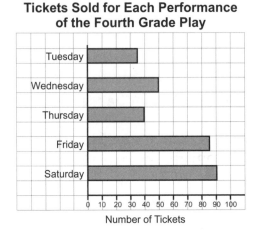

Tickets Sold for Each Performance of the Fourth Grade Play

Pictograph

Symbols are used to show data in a pictograph.
The **key** shows what each symbol stands for.

Bar Graph

Bars are used to show data in a bar graph.
Numbers on the axis represent the scale.

The **range** is the difference between the greatest value and the least value on the graph.
The greatest value on the graphs above is 90. The least value is 35.
$90 - 35 = 55$ So, the range is 55.

Try These

Use the pictograph to answer these questions.

1. Which drink had the most votes? _____

2. Which drink had 12 votes? _____

3. What is the range? _____

Favourite Drinks

Milk	
Juice	
Lemonade	
Water	

☐ = 6 votes

1. This graph shows the number of pet owners in each grade at Parkdale School.
   a) Which grade has the most ~~X~~ pet owners? ___2___
   b) Which grade has one half as many pet owners as Grade 2? ___4___
   c) What is the range of this graph? _____

Pet Owners

Grade 1	🐱🐱🐱🐱🐱🐱
Grade 2	🐱🐱🐱🐱🐱🐱🐱🐱
Grade 3	🐱🐱🐱🐱
Grade 4	🐱🐱
Grade 5	🐱🐱🐱🐱🐱🐱
Grade 6	🐱🐱🐱🐱🐱🐱🐱🐱

 = 4 students

2. This graph shows the types of dwellings the students in Enzo's school live in.
   a) How many students live in condos? ___70___
   b) How many more students live in duplexes than condos? ___60___
   c) How many students live in condos and townhouses altogether? ___40,30___

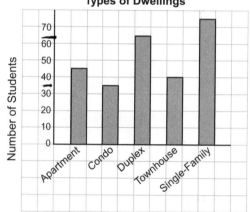

Types of Dwellings

Stretch Your Thinking

How many students attend Enzo's school? Show how you know.

_____

_____

_____

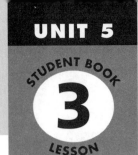
Reading Circle Graphs

Quick Review

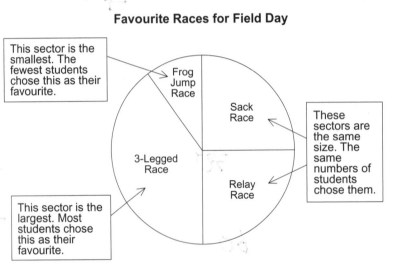

The **circle graph** below shows the race each student in Parker's class chose for Field Day.

A circle graph shows parts of a whole.

In the graph, the circle represents Parker's whole class.

Favourite Races for Field Day

This sector is the smallest. The fewest students chose this as their favourite.

Frog Jump Race

Sack Race

These sectors are the same size. The same numbers of students chose them.

3-Legged Race

Relay Race

This sector is the largest. Most students chose this as their favourite.

Try These

1. What colour hair does the largest number of students have? _____

2. About what fraction of the class has blond hair? _____

3. About what fraction of the class has brown hair? _____

4. Which two hair colours together represent about $\frac{1}{4}$ of the students? _____

Hair Colours of Students in Roni's Class

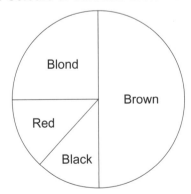

Blond

Brown

Red

Black

1. This circle graph shows how Kareem spent his Saturday afternoon.
   a) Kareem spent the most time doing which activity?

   _____

   Things Kareem Did on Saturday Afternoon

   b) About what fraction of the afternoon did Kareem spend reading?

   _____

   c) Kareem spent about the same time at which two activities?

   _____

2. This circle graph shows the favourite indoor games of students in Thelma's class.
   a) Which games were chosen most often? _____

   b) Which games were chosen least often?

   _____

   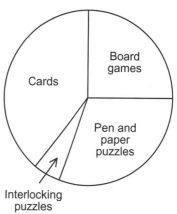

   Favourite Indoor Games

   c) About what fraction of the students chose board games?

   _____

Suppose there are 24 students in Thelma's class.
About how many of them chose board games as their favourite kind of game?

_____

Drawing Pictographs

Quick Review

Here are the results of a survey showing the favourite subjects of students in Kim's class.

Subject	Math	Science	Social Studies	Gym	Writing
Number of Students	6	7	4	5	6

Here's how Kim made a pictograph to display these data.

To make sure her graph was not too large, Kim chose 🚶 to represent 2 students. Kim completed the pictograph with a key, a label on the axis, and a title.

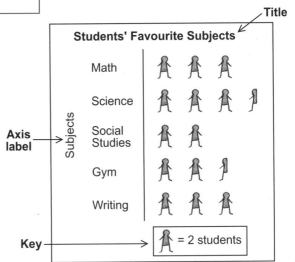

Try These

1. Suppose you drew a pictograph to represent the data in each table. What key would you use for each graph?

a)
Favourite Fruit	Number of Students
Orange	12
Apple	6
Banana	8
Grape	10

b)
Eye Colour	Number of People
Blue	25
Brown	40
Grey	5
Green	15

Key: _____

Key: _____

1. Draw a pictograph to display these data.

Names for Our Fish

	Bubbles	Spotty	Precious	Ralph
Number of students	20	10	5	10

Name for our fish

Bubbles 20
Spotty 10
Precious 5
Ralph 10

2. Finish the pictograph to display the data in the table.

Birds Seen in the Park

Bird	Number
Crow	4
Robin	12
Chickadee	14
Duck	20

Birds Seen in the Park

Crow

Robin

Chickadee

Duck

= 4 birds

Stretch Your Thinking ·

Suppose the key on a pictograph is ◯ = 40 votes.
What symbol would you draw to represent:

10 votes? _____   30 votes? _____

Drawing Bar Graphs

Quick Review

The students in Arnie's school are voting on a mascot for their school hockey team. Here is a table Arnie made to show how they voted.

Animal	Student Votes
Brown bear	40
Cougar	60
Eagle	75
Coyote	35

Here's how to draw a vertical bar graph to display the data in Arnie's table.

1. Draw 2 axes. Label them "Animal" and "Student Votes."
2. Count by 5s for the scale. The scale is 1 square represents 5 votes.
3. Draw a vertical bar for each animal in the table.
4. Write a title for the graph.

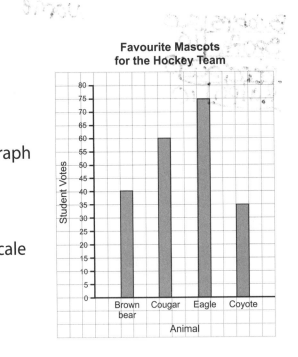

Favourite Mascots for the Hockey Team

Try These

Use the data in this table to complete the graph.

Ice Cream	Number of People
Vanilla	40
Chocolate	75
Strawberry	50

1. Label the axes.
2. Number the scale
3. Give the graph a title.

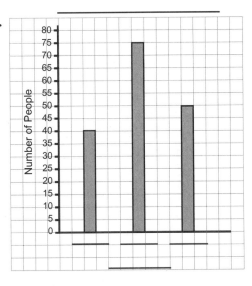

1. The students in Peter's school voted for their favourite type of music. The results are displayed in this table.

Type of Music	Rock	Rap	Hip Hop	Pop
Number of Students	65	70	40	55

a) Draw a vertical bar graph to display these data.

b) Write two things you know from looking at your graph.

_____

_____

Stretch Your Thinking . . . .

Your grid paper has 20 squares along one side. The greatest value you have to display on the graph is 150. What scale will you use? Explain.

_____

_____

UNIT 5

STUDENT BOOK

6

LESSON

Conducting a Survey

Quick Review

You conduct a **survey** to collect and record data on a topic.

Bernie wanted to know how many hours his classmates spent studying for the science test.

He took these steps to conduct a survey.

1. First, Bernie wrote this survey question: "How many hours did you study for the science test?"
2. Next, he drew a table.
3. In the first column, he listed his classmates' possible answers.
4. He asked each classmate his question.
5. He made a tally mark in the second column to record each answer.

Hours	Students
0				
$\frac{1}{2}$	ℍℍ
1	ℍℍ ||||
$1\frac{1}{2}$	|||
2			
$2\frac{1}{2}$		
3	

From the tally chart, Bernie knows that the largest number of his classmates studied 1 hour for the science test.

Try These

1. Write a survey question for each topic.

   a) Number of provinces visited

   _____

   b) Least favourite vegetable

   _____

   c) Favourite pet

   _____

1. a) This tally chart shows the results of
Jose's survey. What question
do you think he asked his classmates?

Aircraft	Number of Students
Hot air balloon	卌 II
Space shuttle	卌 卌 III
Helicopter	卌 II
Glider	III

_____

_____

b) Write three things you know from Jose's tally chart.

_____

_____

_____

_____

2. This graph shows a student's survey results.

a) What might the student's
survey question have been?

_____

b) Write two things you know
from looking at the graph.

_____

_____

_____

_____

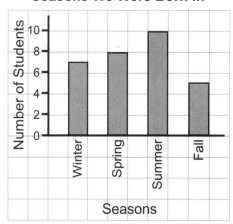

Seasons We Were Born In

Suppose you are surveying your classmates about their favourite fairy tale
character. What would you do if some students gave answers not listed on your
tally chart?

_____

_____

Exploring Units of Time

Quick Review

You can use different units to measure time.

- 1 hour = 60 minutes
- 1 day = 24 hours
- 1 week = 7 days
- 1 month = about 4 weeks

- 1 year = 12 months, 52 weeks, or 365 days
- 1 decade = 10 years
- 1 century = 10 decades or 100 years
- 1 millennium = 10 centuries or 1000 years

Choose a reasonable unit to measure time.
It's more reasonable to say

Lynne rode her bicycle for 2 hours.   than   Lynne rode her bicycle for 120 minutes.

Try These

1. Complete each sentence with the most reasonable unit of time.

   a) The Olympics take place every 4 _____.

   b) Penny speed walks for 30 _____ each day.

   c) Mahood practises on his violin for 1 _____ every night.

2. Write >, <, or = in each box.

   a) 6 decades [ ] 40 years

   b) 2 centuries [ ] 200 years

   c) 1 millennium [ ] 100 years

   d) 15 hours [ ] 1 day

1. Play this game with a partner.

You will need:
2 blank spinners
2 open paper clips to use as pointers
Paper to record your points

➤ Make the two spinners like the ones below.
➤ Each player spins the pointer on his or her spinner.
   Compare the results.
➤ The player with the longer time period gets a point.
➤ If the time periods are equal, both players get a point.
➤ Keep playing until one player has 10 points.

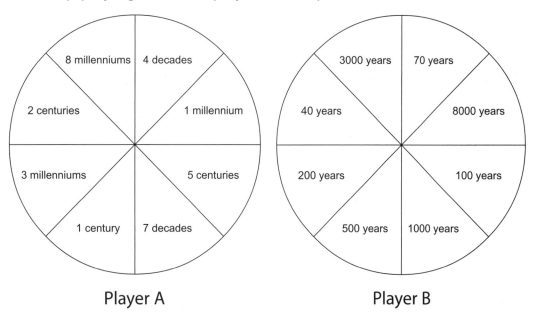

Player A   Player B

Stretch Your Thinking . . . .

Orville and Wilbur Wright took their first flight about 100 years ago.
Write this time period in as many different ways as you can.

_____

_____

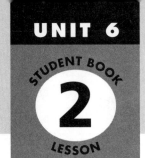

Telling Time

Quick Review

When the minute hand moves from one mark on the clock to the next mark, it takes 1 minute of time.

 9:25

 9:26

You can read times after the half-hour in different ways.

52 minutes after 4 o'clock or 4:52

8 minutes before 5 o'clock or 8 minutes to 5

Try These

1. Write the time shown on each clock.

a)

b)

c)

_____   _____   _____

2. Show the time on each clock.

a)

9:58

b)

3:39

c)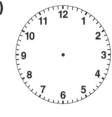

10:21

1. Write each time in two ways.
    a)

    b)

    _____

    _____

    _____

    _____

2. Show the time on each digital clock.
    a) quarter to five   b) half past eleven   c) quarter past six

   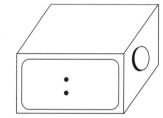   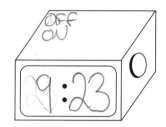

3. Write something you might be doing at each time.

    a) 12:04 p.m. _____

    b) 3:58 a.m. _____

The sum of the digits on this digital clock is 15.
At what other times will the digits add up to 15?
Give at least 2 answers.

_____

Estimating Time

Quick Review

One small unit of time is a **minute**.

It takes about
1 minute to count
to 100.

It takes about
5 minutes to eat
an apple.

It takes about
15 minutes to play
a game of Go Fish.

Try These

1. Circle the better estimate for how long each activity would take.

   a) Make a peanut butter sandwich.   2 minutes or 15 minutes

   b) Take a shower.   10 minutes or 20 minutes

   c) Walk the dog.   20 minutes or 4 hours

   d) Sing "O Canada."   15 minutes or 2 minutes

2. Write how long it takes the minute hand to move

   from    to

1. Work with a partner.
Take turns.
> ➤ Choose an activity from the chart.
> ➤ Estimate how long it will take to do the activity.
>   Record your estimate.
> ➤ Have your partner time you while you do the activity.
>   Record the time to the nearest minute.

Activity	Estimated Time	Actual Time
Count back by 2s from 99 to 1.		
Find the word *spider* in a dictionary.		
Draw 50 happy faces. 😊		
Measure the length of the room.		
Multiply 27 × 8.		

Stretch Your Thinking

Lee leaves for school at 8:10 a.m.
He needs to do his chores before he leaves.
At about what time do you think he should
start his chores? Explain.

> **Lee's Morning Chores**
>
> Make the bed ✔
> Feed the dog ✔
> Pack lunch ✔

_____

_____

_____

Exploring Elapsed Time

Quick Review

You arrive at the park at 12:25 p.m.

You can spend 3 hours and 30 minutes there.

Here's how to find out what time to leave the park.

Start at 12:25 and add 3 hours.   Then add 30 minutes.

   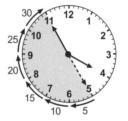

12:25 p.m. ⟶ 3:25 p.m.   3:25 p.m. ⟶ 3:55 p.m.

You will leave the park at 3:55 p.m.
The time between 12:25 p.m. and 3:55 p.m. is the **elapsed time**.

Try These

Show the end time on each clock.

1. Rapi's guitar lesson started at 7:15.
   It lasted for 40 minutes.

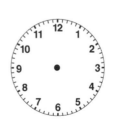

2. The ball game started at 1:30 p.m.
   It lasted 1 hour and 20 minutes.

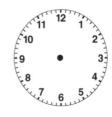

1. Write each elapsed time.

   a) 6:45 a.m. to 7:58 a.m. _____

   b) 10:08 a.m. to 1:30 p.m. _____

   c) 3:17 p.m. to 7:47 p.m. _____

2. The hot air balloon ride is 1 hour and 20 minutes long.
   Complete the table to show the end time for each ride.

   Balloon Rides

	Take-off Time	End Time
a)	7:45 a.m.	
b)	12:15 p.m.	
c)	2:00 p.m.	

3. How much time is there between the start of the second ride and the

   start of the third ride? _____

4. Keisha left home at 11:20. She got to the balloon rides at 1:15.

   How long did it take Keisha to get there? _____

Stretch Your Thinking

Find out the sunrise and sunset times for today.
Record the times, and find the elapsed time between them.

_____

_____

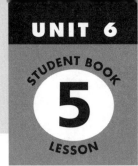
Estimating and Counting Money

Quick Review

Here's a way to count money.

First, sort the dollars and count them.

Count: "10, ...   12,   14,   16 ... **17 dollars**," or $17

Then, make as many one-dollar groups as you can. Count them.

Count: "1,   ...   2,   ...   **3 dollars**," or $3

Finally, count the rest of the coins.

Count: "5,   ...   6,   ...   7,   ...   **8 cents**," or $0.08

You have: $17 + $3 + $0.08 = $20.08

Try These

1. Estimate, then count.
   Write each estimate and amount.

   a)

   _____

   b)

   _____

1. Draw pictures to show each amount.
   Use the least number of bills and coins.

   a) $27.78

   b) $48.39

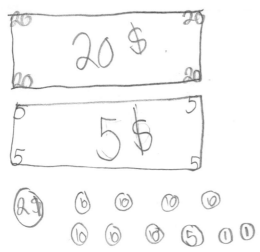

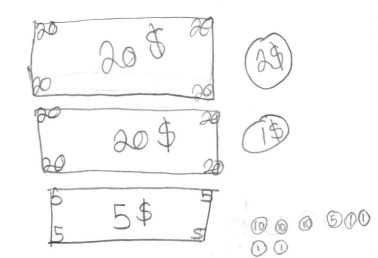

2. Show three different ways to make $17.23.

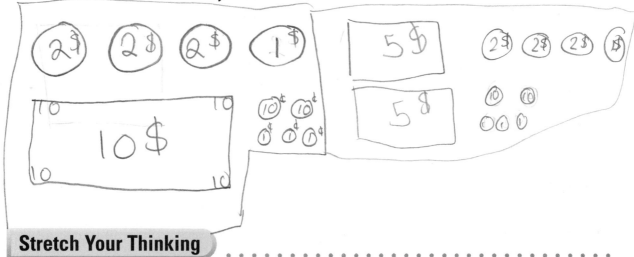

Olivia has 10 coins: some toonies, some loonies, and some quarters.
She has more toonies than loonies, and more loonies than quarters.
How much money does Olivia have? Explain.

_____

_____

_____

_____

Making Change

Quick Review

Harvey bought a DVD for $23.89.
He used a $20 bill and a $10 bill to pay for it.
Here's how the clerk made change for him:
"That's $23.89 …

   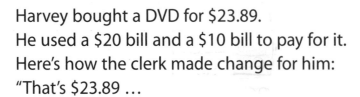

$23.90 … $24.00 … $25.00 … $30.00"

Harvey got $6.11 in change.
Harvey estimated to make sure he got the correct change.

He thought:

The DVD cost about $24.
Thirty dollars minus $24 is $6.
That's the same as $6.11
rounded to the nearest dollar.

Try These

1. Draw pictures to show the change for each purchase.
   a) Arlene paid for this helmet with two $10 bills.

$14.49

   b) Jasper paid for these hiking boots with a
   $20 bill and two $10 bills.

$32.25

1. Draw pictures to show the change for each purchase.
   Write the amount.

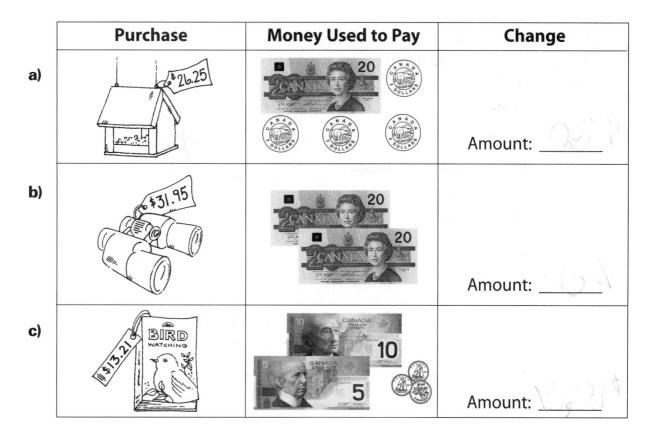

	Purchase	Money Used to Pay	Change
a)	$26.25	20 CANADA 2 DOLLARS (coins)	Amount: _____
b)	$31.95	20 CANADA, 20 CANADA	Amount: _____
c)	BIRD WATCHING $13.21	10 CANADA, 5 CANADA (coins)	Amount: _____

2. Jen bought a CD for $17.59. She paid with a $20 bill.
   She got $2.31 change. Did Jen get the right change? Explain.

_____

Juanita paid for a hummingbird feeder and
a bottle of nectar solution with a $50 bill.
About how much change did she get?

$8.29 $6.75   Nectar

_____

Measuring Capacity

Quick Review

The amount that a container can hold is its **capacity**.
Units used to measure capacity are the **litre** (L) and the **millilitre** (mL).

1 L = 1000 mL

This carton has a capacity
of one litre.
It holds 1 L of juice.

This can has a capacity of
three hundred fifty-five millilitres.
It holds 355 mL of ice tea.

Try These

1. Would you use millilitres or litres to measure each capacity?

   a)

   b)

   c)

   _____   _____   _____

2. Circle the better estimate for each capacity.

   a)

   b)

   c)

   200 mL or 900 mL   40 mL or 4 L   1000 mL or 1000 L

1. Number the containers from the least to the greatest capacity.

TOMATO JUICE 945 mL Vinegar 4 L Vanilla 280 mL Bleach 1 L

☐　☐　☐　☐

2. a) Complete the table.

L	1	2	3				
mL	1000						

b) What pattern do you see in the table?

_____

_____

3. Find four items at home with capacities shown in millilitres and litres.
List the items and their capacities in order from greatest to least capacity.

　　Item　　　　　　　　　　　　　　　Capacity

1) _____

2) _____

3) _____

4) _____

Stretch Your Thinking

Suppose you are making pudding.
The recipe calls for 500 mL of milk.
You have a 1 L carton of milk.
How much milk will be left over? _____

Measuring Mass

Quick Review

The mass of an object is a measure of how heavy it is.

The **gram** (g) and the **kilogram** (kg) are units used to measure mass.

The **gram** is used to measure light objects.

The **kilogram** is used to measure heavier objects.

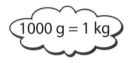

1000 g = 1 kg

The mass of a $5 bill is about 1 g.

The mass of one litre of milk is about 1 kg.

> ## Try These

1. Would you use grams or kilograms to measure each mass?

   a)

   b)

   c)

   _____   _____   _____

2. Circle the better estimate for each mass.

   a)

   b)

   c)

   150 g or 950 g   110 g or 2 kg   30 kg or 1000 kg

Complete.

1. **a)** 3 kg = _____ g   **b)** 7 kg = _____ g   **c)** 4 kg = _____ g

   d) 2000 g = _____ kg   **e)** 8000 g = _____ kg   **f)** 5000 g = _____ kg

2. Number the objects from least to greatest mass.

☐   ☐   ☐   ☐

3. Find four items at home with masses shown in grams and kilograms.
List the items and their masses in order from greatest to least.

   Item   Mass

   1) _____

   2) _____

   3) _____

   4) _____

Stretch Your Thinking . . . .

Sandar, Belinda, and Gloria together have a mass of 89 kg.
Sandar and Belinda together have a mass of 62 kg.
Sandar and Gloria together have a mass of 57 kg.
What is each child's mass? Show your work.

_____

Grids and Coordinates

Quick Review

This map of Cape Breton Island in Nova Scotia is drawn on a **grid**.

➤ The squares along the bottom of the grid are labelled with letters.

➤ The squares along the side of the grid are labelled with numbers.

➤ Use a letter and a number to locate any square.

These letter and number combinations are called **coordinates**.
Big Pond is located at C2.

Try These •

Use the map of Cape Breton Island. List the coordinates of each place.

1. a) Grace Bay _____   **b)** Port Hood _____

   c) Cape North _____   **d)** Port Hawkesbury _____

   e) Inverness _____   **f)** Cape Breton Highlands National Park _____

1. List the coordinates of each word.

   a) car _____   **b)** bus _____

   c) taxi _____   **d)** bike _____

2. Name the word in each square.

   a) F3 _____   **b)** A2 _____

   c) D4 _____   **d)** C2 _____

6					bus	
5			car			
4		bike		plane		
3						truck
2	van		train			
1				taxi		
	A	B	C	D	E	F

3. Play this game with a partner.
   You will need:
   1 cube numbered 1 to 6
   1 cube labelled A to F
   2 different-coloured counters

   ➤ Take turns rolling the cubes
     to get a pair of coordinates.
   ➤ Cover the square on the grid
     with one of your counters.
   ➤ If the square is already
     covered, you lose your turn.
   ➤ Continue playing until all the
     squares are covered.
   ➤ The player who covers the
     most squares wins.

Stretch Your Thinking

Write the directions for a new game to play on a grid.

_____

_____

_____

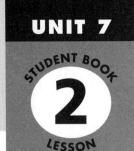
Translations

At Home
At School

Quick Review

A figure is **translated** when it moves along a straight line from one position to another.
The move, or slide, is called a **translation**.
The figure does not turn or flip.

This figure has been translated
2 squares right and
2 squares down.
Whenever you describe a translation, say how many squares left or right, and then say how many
up or down.

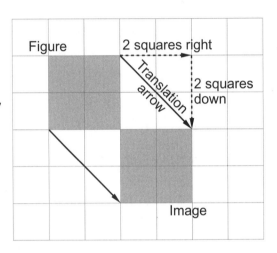

Translation arrows join matching points on the figure and its **image**.
The figure and its image are congruent.

Try These

1. Do these pictures show translations? Write *Yes* or *No*.

   a)

   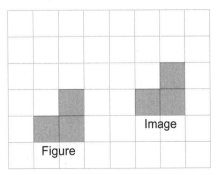

   b)

   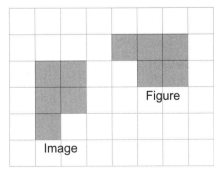

   _____

   _____

1. Translate each figure. Draw the image and the translation arrow.

   a) 3 squares right and
   2 squares up

   b) 4 squares left and
   2 squares down

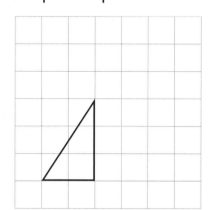
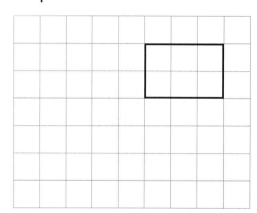

2. Translate the figure three times. Draw the images and the translation arrows.
   Label your translations A, B, and C.

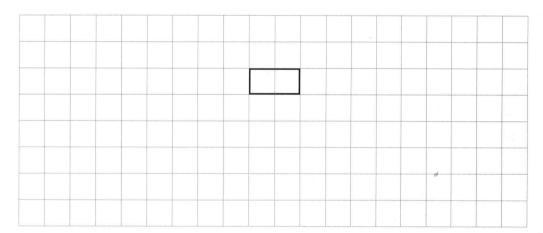

How would you describe your translations in question 2?

_____

_____

_____

_____

Reflections

Quick Review

This picture shows the **reflection of a figure in a mirror line.**

The figure and its image are congruent.

The figure and its image are the same distance from the mirror line.

The two figures face opposite directions.

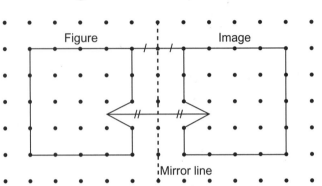

Figure   Image

Mirror line

Try These

1. Do these pictures show reflections? Write *Yes* or *No.*

   a)

   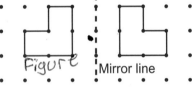

   Figure   Mirror line

   yes

   b)

   Mirror line

   yes

   c)

   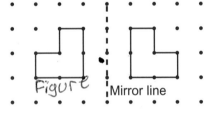

   Mirror line

   yes

   d)

   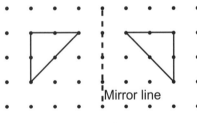

   Mirror line

   _No_

1. Draw each reflection image.

   a)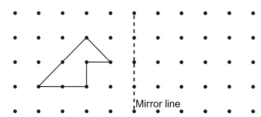

   b)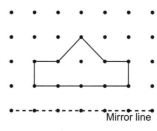

2. Work with a partner.
   Draw a mirror line in part a.
   Draw a figure on one side of the mirror line.
   Have your partner draw its reflection image.
   Repeat for part b, but switch roles.

   a)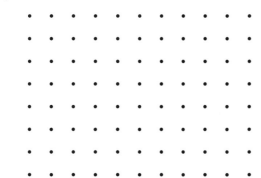

   b)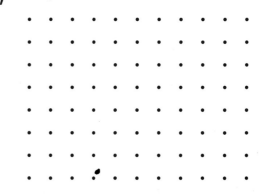

The top figure shown here
is a reflection image of
the bottom figure.
Draw the mirror line.

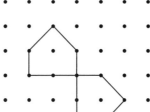

Lines of Symmetry

Quick Review

At Home
At School

A **line of symmetry** divides a figure into two parts that are congruent.

When a line of symmetry can be drawn on a figure, it has **symmetry**.

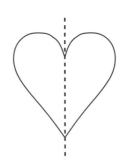

Some figures do not have a line of symmetry.

Some figures have more than one line of symmetry.

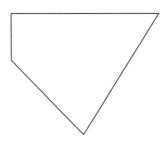 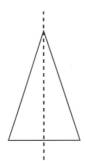 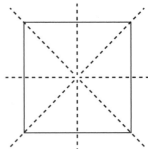

0 lines of symmetry   1 line of symmetry   4 lines of symmetry

Try These

1. Is each broken line a line of symmetry? Write *Yes* or *No*.

a)

b)

c)

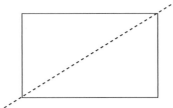

_____   _____   _____

1. Draw as many lines of symmetry on each figure as you can.

   a)

   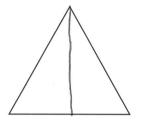

   b)

   c)

   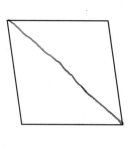

2. Work with a partner.

   Each of you draw one half of a design on one side of the line of symmetry on your grid. Switch places and complete your partner's design.

   Your Grid

   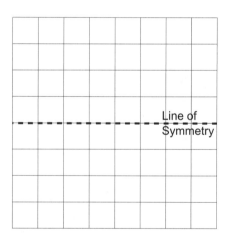

   Your Partner's Grid

   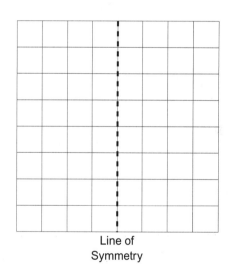

   Line of Symmetry

Complete the figure to make it symmetrical.

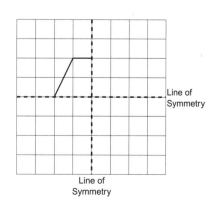

Line of Symmetry

Rotations

Quick Review

A **rotation** is a turn about a **turn centre**.

When a figure is rotated, its image is congruent to the figure.

The rotation can be clockwise.

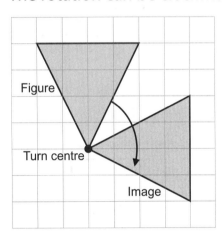

The rotation can be counterclockwise.

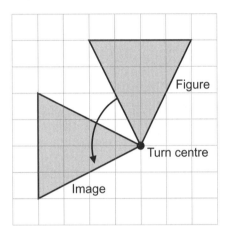

This triangle has rotated $\frac{1}{4}$ of a turn clockwise.

This triangle has rotated $\frac{1}{4}$ of a turn counterclockwise.

Translations, reflections, and rotations are all called **transformations**.

Try These

1. Draw the image of each figure after a $\frac{1}{4}$ turn, a $\frac{1}{2}$ turn, and a $\frac{3}{4}$ turn.

   a)

   b)

   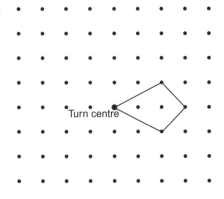

Practice

1. Draw the image of each figure after each rotation.

   a) $\frac{1}{4}$ turn counterclockwise

   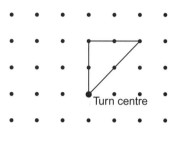

   b) $\frac{1}{2}$ turn clockwise

   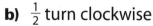
   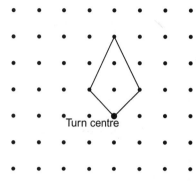

2. Each picture shows a transformation. Name the transformation.

   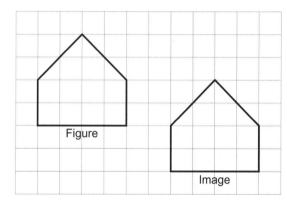
   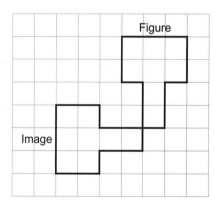

   a) _____

   b) _____

Stretch Your Thinking

Can you tell which transformation
has been performed? Explain.

_____

_____

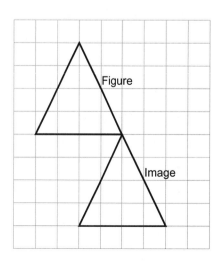

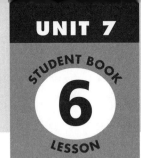

UNIT 7

STUDENT BOOK **6** LESSON

Patterns with Transformations

At Home At School

Quick Review

You can use transformations to make a pattern.

➤ Here is a pattern in a straight line.
It was made with $\frac{1}{2}$ turn rotations and reflections.

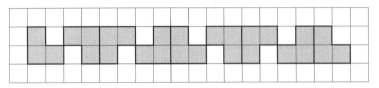

➤ Here is an **area pattern**. An area pattern covers a region.
It was made with translations and reflections.

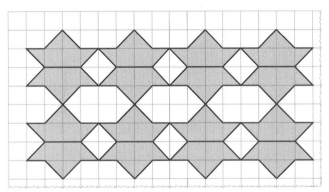

Try This

Which transformations were used to make this pattern?

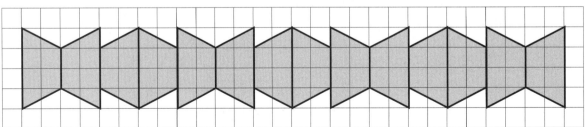

_____

_____

114

Practice

1. **a)** Use this figure and transformations to make a pattern in a line.

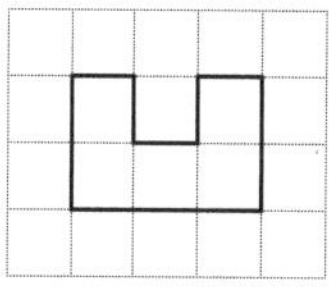

b) Describe the transformations you used.

2. **a)** Use this figure and transformations to make an area pattern.

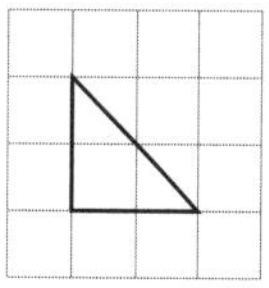

b) Describe the transformations you used.

Stretch Your Thinking

Name some places where you might see an area pattern.

Fractions of a Whole

At Home
At School

Quick Review

➤ Fractions describe equal parts of a whole.

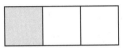 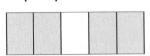 

3 equal parts
are thirds.
$\frac{1}{3}$ is shaded.

5 equal parts
are fifths.
$\frac{4}{5}$ are shaded.

8 equal parts are eighths.
$\frac{5}{8}$ are shaded.

The **denominator** tells
how many equal parts
are in 1 whole.

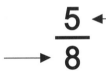
5 ←
8

The **numerator** tells
how many equal parts
are counted.

➤ A proper fraction represents an amount less than 1 whole.
$\frac{5}{8}$ is a proper fraction.

Try These

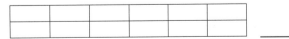

1. Write a fraction to tell what part of each figure is shaded.

   a) _____

   b) _____

   c) _____

2. Colour some of the equal parts of each figure.
   Write a fraction to describe the coloured parts.

   a) _____

   b) _____

   c)  _____

Play this game with a partner.
You will need:
2 number cubes
2 pencil crayons or crayons of different colours

Take turns making fractions.

➤ Roll the number cubes. Use the greater number as the denominator.

➤ Find a figure on the game board that can be used to show your fraction. Colour the figure. Write the fraction.

➤ If there is no figure that can be used, you lose your turn.

➤ Keep playing until all the figures are coloured.

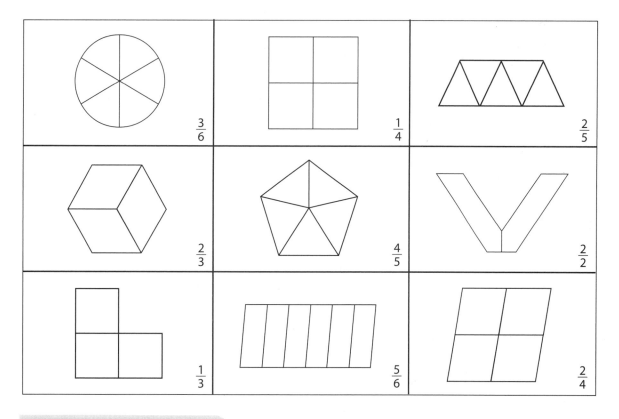

Stretch Your Thinking

This figure represents $\frac{3}{5}$ of one whole.
Show what the whole might look like.

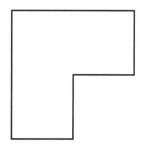

Fraction Benchmarks

Quick Review

You can use the benchmarks of $0, \frac{1}{2}$, and 1 to tell about how big a fraction is.

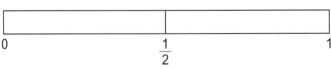

$\frac{7}{8}$ is closer to 1.

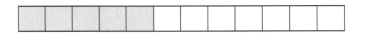

$\frac{5}{12}$ is closer to $\frac{1}{2}$.

It is a little less than $\frac{1}{2}$.

$\frac{2}{12}$ is closer to 0.

Try These

1. Colour each strip to show a fraction.
   Write whether the fraction is closer to $0, \frac{1}{2}$, or 1.

a)

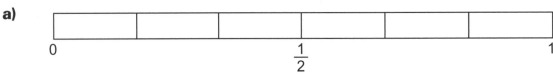

Closer to _____

b)

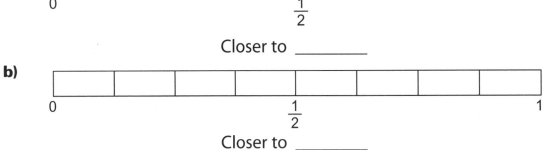

Closer to _____

2. A trashcan is not quite full. Write a fraction that might tell how full it is.

_____

Play this game with a partner.

You will need:
Index cards with these fractions written on them:

$\frac{1}{3}, \frac{2}{3}, \frac{1}{5}, \frac{2}{5}, \frac{3}{5}, \frac{4}{5}, \frac{1}{6}, \frac{2}{6}, \frac{4}{6}, \frac{5}{6}, \frac{1}{8}, \frac{2}{8}, \frac{3}{8}, \frac{5}{8}, \frac{6}{8}, \frac{7}{8}, \frac{1}{12}, \frac{2}{12}, \frac{4}{12}, \frac{5}{12}, \frac{7}{12}, \frac{8}{12}, \frac{10}{12}, \frac{11}{12}$

A paper bag
Strips of paper 15 cm long
Crayons

Put the fraction cards in the bag.
Take turns.
➤ Draw a card from the bag.
➤ Estimate whether the fraction is closer to 0, $\frac{1}{2}$, or 1.
➤ Fold and colour a paper strip to show the fraction.
➤ Line up your strip with this number line to check your estimate.

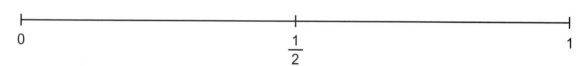

➤ You get a point if your estimate was right.
➤ Your partner gets a point if your estimate was wrong.
➤ Keep playing until one player has 10 points.

Stretch Your Thinking . . . .

1. Name a fraction between 0 and $\frac{1}{2}$ that is neither closer to 0 nor closer to $\frac{1}{2}$.

   _____

2. Name a fraction that is between $\frac{1}{2}$ and 1 that is neither closer to $\frac{1}{2}$ nor closer to 1.

   _____

Fractions of a Set

Quick Review

You can use fractions to show equal parts of a set.

○ ○ } $\frac{1}{4}$ of 8 = 2

○ ○
○ ○ } $\frac{3}{4}$ of 8 = 6

○ ○

$\frac{4}{4}$ of 8 = 8

Here is a way to find $\frac{5}{6}$ of 18.

The denominator lets us know we are counting sixths. Divide 18 counters into 6 equal groups to show sixths.

○ ○ ○ ○ ○ ○
○ ○ ○ ○ ○ ○
○ ○ ○ ○ ○ ○
$\frac{1}{6}$ $\frac{1}{6}$ $\frac{1}{6}$ $\frac{1}{6}$ $\frac{1}{6}$ $\frac{1}{6}$

$\frac{1}{6}$ of 18 = 3 $\frac{5}{6}$ of 18 = 15

Try These

Draw a picture to show the fraction of each set.

$\frac{1}{2}$ of 10 = _____	$\frac{2}{3}$ of 9 = _____
$\frac{4}{5}$ of 15 = _____	$\frac{1}{4}$ of 12 = _____

1. Write a fraction for the shaded part of each set.

   a)

   Fell, camte, fell

   b)

   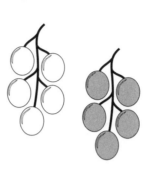

   camte, fell

   c)

   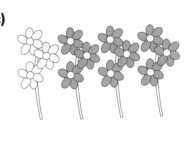

   camtyfell, fdl, fell

2. Use counters to find the fraction of each set.

   a) $\frac{1}{2}$ of 14 = ____17____   b) $\frac{2}{6}$ of 18 = _____   c) $\frac{3}{5}$ of 15 = _____

   d) $\frac{3}{8}$ of 16 = _____   e) $\frac{3}{4}$ of 12 = _____   f) $\frac{6}{10}$ of 20 = _____

   g) $\frac{7}{7}$ of 14 = _____   h) $\frac{7}{8}$ of 24 = _____   I) $\frac{2}{3}$ of 15 = _____

3. On Pet Day, 18 children brought a pet to school.
   Two thirds of the pets were dogs. One ninth of the pets were cats.

   a) How many dogs were there? _____

   b) How many cats were there? _____

   c) How many animals were neither dogs nor cats? _____

Stretch Your Thinking

1. Choose letters from the box.

   a) Write a word that uses $\frac{1}{2}$ of the letters.

   _____

   b) Write a word that uses $\frac{3}{5}$ of the letters.

   _____

   A I   T

   M U L

   R

   O E S

Different Names for Fractions

At Home
At School

Quick Review

Equivalent fractions are fractions that name the same amount.

1 Whole					
$\frac{1}{2}$			$\frac{1}{2}$		
$\frac{1}{6}$	$\frac{1}{6}$	$\frac{1}{6}$	$\frac{1}{6}$	$\frac{1}{6}$	$\frac{1}{6}$

1 Whole							
$\frac{1}{2}$				$\frac{1}{2}$			
$\frac{1}{4}$		$\frac{1}{4}$		$\frac{1}{4}$		$\frac{1}{4}$	
$\frac{1}{8}$	$\frac{1}{8}$	$\frac{1}{8}$	$\frac{1}{8}$	$\frac{1}{8}$	$\frac{1}{8}$	$\frac{1}{8}$	$\frac{1}{8}$

$\frac{1}{2}$ and $\frac{3}{6}$ are equivalent fractions.

$\frac{3}{4}$ and $\frac{6}{8}$ are equivalent fractions.

Try These

1. Write an equivalent fraction for each fraction.

1 Whole									
$\frac{1}{5}$		$\frac{1}{5}$		$\frac{1}{5}$		$\frac{1}{5}$		$\frac{1}{5}$	
$\frac{1}{10}$	$\frac{1}{10}$	$\frac{1}{10}$	$\frac{1}{10}$	$\frac{1}{10}$	$\frac{1}{10}$	$\frac{1}{10}$	$\frac{1}{10}$	$\frac{1}{10}$	$\frac{1}{10}$

a) $\frac{1}{5}$ _____   b) $\frac{2}{5}$ _____   c) $\frac{3}{5}$ _____   d) $\frac{4}{5}$ _____   e) $\frac{5}{5}$ _____

2. Write equivalent fractions to name the shaded part of each figure.

a)   b) 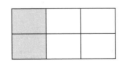   c)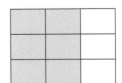

_____   _____   _____

1. Fold paper strips to find an equivalent fraction for each fraction.

   a) $\frac{3}{6}$ _9_ b) $\frac{1}{2}$ _3_ c) $\frac{2}{4}$ _6_

   d) $\frac{3}{3}$ _6_ e) $\frac{3}{4}$ _7_ f) $\frac{2}{8}$ _10_

2. a) A pizza is divided into 12 equal slices.
   4 slices have mushrooms only.
   6 slices have pepperoni only.
   2 slices have mushrooms and pepperoni.
   Write two equivalent fractions to describe
   the parts of the pizza with

   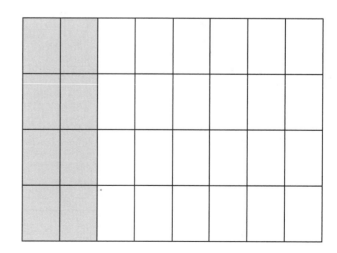

   mushrooms only: _$\frac{4}{}$_ and _$\frac{1}{2}$_

   pepperoni only: _$\frac{3}{6}$_ and _$\frac{1}{2}$_

   mushrooms and pepperoni: _$\frac{1}{2}$_ and _0_

   b) Nine slices of pizza were eaten.

   Write two equivalent fractions for this amount. _____ and _____
   Write two equivalent fractions for how much pizza was not eaten.

   _12_ and _0_

Use the diagram.
Write four equivalent fractions to
name the shaded part.

_____ _____

_____ _____

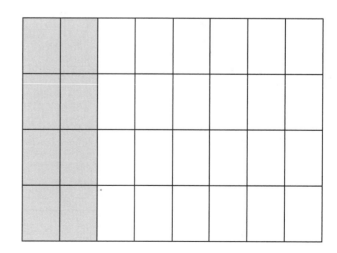

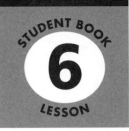
More than One

Quick Review

Tyla arranged 7 trapezoids.

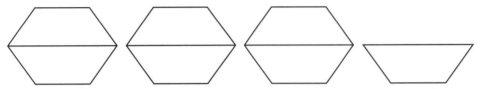

Her arrangement shows seven halves of a hexagon: $\frac{7}{2}$

It also shows three whole hexagons plus 1 half: $3\frac{1}{2}$

$\frac{7}{2}$ and $3\frac{1}{2}$ describe the same amount.

An **improper fraction** shows an amount greater than 1 whole. $\frac{7}{2}$ is an improper fraction.

A **mixed number** has a whole number part and a fraction part. $3\frac{1}{2}$ is a mixed number.

Try These . . . .

1. Write an improper fraction and a mixed number for each picture.

   a)

   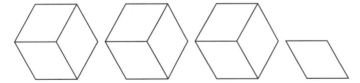

   _____

   b)

   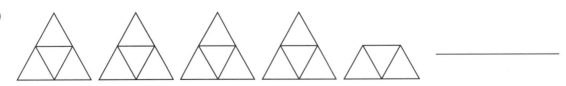

   _____

   c)

   _____

1. Draw pictures to show each improper fraction.
Write the mixed number.

$\frac{5}{2}$ _____	$\frac{7}{3}$ _____

2. Draw pictures to show each mixed number.
Write the improper fraction.

$4\frac{1}{4}$ _____	$2\frac{6}{8}$ _____

3. Sofia took piano lessons for 18 months.
How many years is that? Show your work.

_____

_____

Stretch Your Thinking . . . .

Henry drank 4 glasses of juice. Ethan drank $\frac{9}{2}$ glasses of juice.
Who drank more juice? Explain how you know.

_____

_____

_____

UNIT 8

STUDENT BOOK 7 LESSON

Comparing and Ordering Fractions

Quick Review

➤ You can compare fractions that have the same denominator. Each part being counted is the same size.

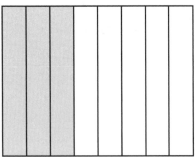 $\frac{3}{8}$ 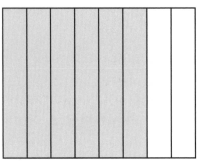 $\frac{6}{8}$

The fewer the parts, the smaller the fraction, so $\frac{3}{8} < \frac{6}{8}$

➤ You can order mixed numbers. First, order according to the whole number part, then the fraction part. $3\frac{4}{8}$, $2\frac{7}{8}$, $3\frac{1}{8}$

From least to greatest: $2\frac{7}{8}$, $3\frac{1}{8}$, $3\frac{4}{8}$

➤ When different fractions have the same numerator, the parts have different sizes.

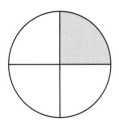 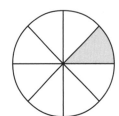

To compare $\frac{1}{4}$ and $\frac{1}{8}$, think about sharing 1 whole. One fourth gives you a bigger piece. So, $\frac{1}{4} > \frac{1}{8}$

Try These

1. Compare the fraction parts.
   Write a fraction sentence about the shaded parts using < or >.
   a)   b)   c)

   _____   _____   _____

126

1. Work with a partner.

   You will need crayons and four strips of paper of the same length for each person.

   ➤ Each of you folds a strip into any number of equal parts. Colour some of the parts to show a fraction.
   ➤ Show your strip to your partner and name the fraction.
   ➤ Compare the fractions by lining the strips up one below the other.
   ➤ On the lines below, record a fraction sentence using >, <, or =.
   ➤ Repeat with three more pairs of strips.

   a) _____   b) _____

   c) _____   d) _____

2. Order these numbers from least to greatest.

   a) $\frac{7}{8}, \frac{14}{8}, \frac{3}{8}$ _____   b) $\frac{9}{10}, \frac{4}{10}, \frac{6}{10}$ _____

   c) $2\frac{4}{6}, \frac{3}{6}, 4\frac{1}{6}$ _____   d) $4\frac{3}{7}, 2\frac{6}{7}, 4\frac{4}{7}$ _____

3. Stivi and Zach shared a pizza.
   Stivi ate $\frac{7}{12}$ of the pizza and Zach ate the rest.
   Who ate more? Explain.

   _____

Stretch Your Thinking

1. Write a fraction or a mixed number to make each statement true.

   a) $\frac{8}{9} >$ ____   b) $1\frac{1}{2} <$ ____   c) ____ $> \frac{3}{8}$ d) $\frac{13}{7} <$ ____

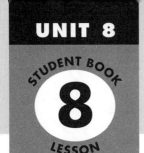
Exploring Tenths

At Home
At School

Quick Review

You can model $1\frac{3}{10}$ with Base Ten Blocks.

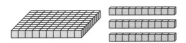

➤ You can write the number as a **decimal** using a symbol, the **decimal point**.
The decimal point always comes right after the whole number.

$1\frac{3}{10}$ is the same as 1.3.

The decimal point separates the whole number from the fraction part.

➤ You can also use a place value chart to show a decimal.

Ones	Tenths
0	8

In the decimal 0.8 there are no whole number parts, only tenths.

Try These

1. Write a fraction or mixed number and a decimal for the shaded part of each picture.

   a)  _____

   b)  _____

   c)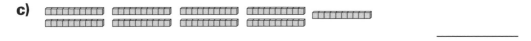
   _____

2. Write each fraction or mixed number as a decimal.

   a) $5\frac{7}{10}$ _____   b) $2\frac{2}{10}$ _____   c) $\frac{8}{10}$ _____

1. Play this game with a partner.
You will need:

24 small counters   1 number cube   2 game markers

Player A strip (left): $4\frac{8}{10}$, $3\frac{6}{10}$, $2\frac{9}{10}$, $2\frac{4}{10}$, $1\frac{5}{10}$, $\frac{9}{10}$, $\frac{7}{10}$, $\frac{6}{10}$, $\frac{4}{10}$, $\frac{3}{10}$, $\frac{2}{10}$, $\frac{1}{10}$

Player A

Player B strip (right): $4\frac{8}{10}$, $3\frac{6}{10}$, $2\frac{9}{10}$, $2\frac{4}{10}$, $1\frac{5}{10}$, $\frac{9}{10}$, $\frac{7}{10}$, $\frac{6}{10}$, $\frac{4}{10}$, $\frac{3}{10}$, $\frac{2}{10}$, $\frac{1}{10}$

Player B

Gameboard top: 2.9 | 0.2 | 2.4 | 0.9 | 4.8
Gameboard left side: 1.5, 0.6, 0.7, 0.1, 2.4, 0.2
Gameboard right side: 0.7, 0.4, 3.6, 0.9, 0.6, 0.3
Gameboard bottom: 0.2 | 4.8 | START | 1.5 | 0.3

Each player selects a strip to the right or the left of the gameboard. The object of the game is to play until one of you covers all of the numbers on your strip.

➤ Put your markers on Start.
➤ Take turns rolling the number cube. Move that number of spaces in either direction.
➤ Put a counter on your strip on the number that names the same amount as the decimal you landed on.
➤ The first one to cover a full strip wins.

Stretch Your Thinking

Karen said point A on the number line shows 2.0. Is she correct? Explain.

_____

_____

_____

Exploring Hundredths

Quick Review

Hundredths can be shown in different ways.

Each of these represents the same amount.

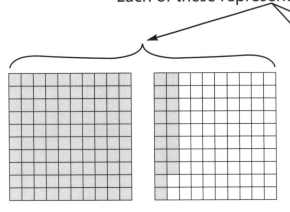

$1\frac{18}{100}$ 1.18

one and eighteen hundredths

Try These

1. Write a fraction or mixed number and a decimal for the shaded part of each picture.

   a)

   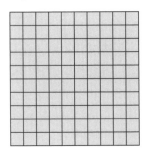

   _____

   b)

   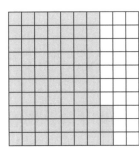

   _____

2. Write each fraction or mixed number as a decimal.

   a) $\frac{48}{100}$ _____

   b) $3\frac{7}{100}$ _____

   c) $\frac{6}{100}$ _____

   d) $6\frac{17}{100}$ _____

   e) $\frac{67}{100}$ _____

   f) $2\frac{5}{100}$ _____

Practice

1. Colour the grids to show the numbers.
   a) 0.09   b) 1.43   c) $\frac{70}{100}$

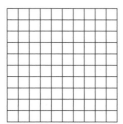 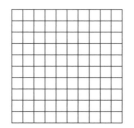 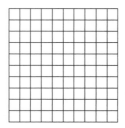 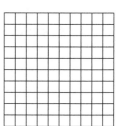

2. Write each decimal as a fraction or a mixed number.

   a) 7.24 _____   b) 6.93 _____

   c) 3.80 _____   d) 0.27 _____

   e) 2.01 _____   f) 2.4 _____

3. Draw pictures of Base Ten Blocks to show each decimal.
   Draw squares, sticks, and dots to represent the blocks.

2.23	1.08

Stretch Your Thinking

Carlos said that 1.30 is greater than 1.3 because 30 is greater than 3.
Is he correct? Use pictures to support your answer.

_____

_____

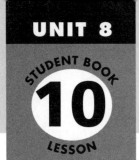
Comparing and Ordering Decimals

Quick Review

Here are the top three results of a track meet event.
You can put these results in order by colouring hundredths grids.
Then, put the distances in order from greatest to least.

Standing Long Jump

Name	Distance
Noor	0.74 m
Laureen	0.72 m
Pat	0.81 m

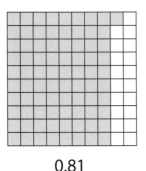
0.81

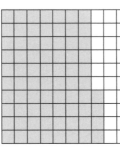
0.74

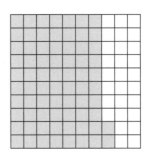
0.72

The best result is the longest jump.
So Pat had the best jump, then Noor, then Laureen.

Try These

1. Circle the greater decimal in each pair.

    a) 0.45 or 0.37   b) 0.19 or 0.82   c) 0.21 or 0.04

    d) 2.06 or 3.02   e) 2.50 or 2.05   f) 7.80 or 7.41

2. Put these decimals in order from least to greatest.

    a) 0.71, 1.09, 0.84 _____

    b) 13.40, 13.32, 12.90 _____

    c) 2.60, 0.75, 4.31 _____

1. Play this game with a partner.
   You will need:
   2 sets of 10 small cards numbered 0 to 9, in a paper bag

   ➤ Take turns drawing a card from the bag.
     After each turn write the digit in any box in Row 1.
     Return the card to the bag.
   ➤ Continue until all 3 boxes are full.
   ➤ Compare your numbers.
       The player with the lesser number wins a point.
   ➤ Play four more rounds.
   ➤ The player with the highest score wins.

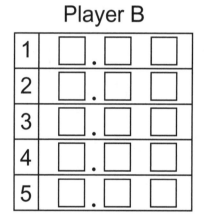

2. a) Put the decimals you made in order from greatest to least.

   _____

   b) Put the decimals your partner made in order from least to greatest.

   _____

Stretch Your Thinking ·

Make up another version of the game. Describe the rules.
Challenge a classmate to play your version.

_____

_____

Adding Decimals

Quick Review

You can use whole number strategies to add decimals.

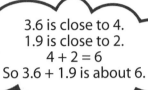

3.6 is close to 4.
1.9 is close to 2.
$4 + 2 = 6$
So $3.6 + 1.9$ is about 6.

➤ Use rounding to estimate $3.6 + 1.9$.
The sum of 3.6 and 1.9 is about 6.

➤ Use Base Ten Blocks to add.

Ones	Tenths		Ones	Tenths
3.6		10 tenths equals 1 whole.		
1.9				

➤ Use place value to add.

Add the tenths: 15 tenths	10 tenths equals 1 whole. That's 1 and 5 tenths.	Add the ones.
$\begin{array}{r} 3.\mathbf{6} \\ + 1.\mathbf{9} \\ \hline \end{array}$	$\begin{array}{r} {}^{1}\\ 3.6 \\ + 1.9 \\ \hline .5 \end{array}$	$\begin{array}{r} {}^{1}\\ \mathbf{3}.6 \\ + \mathbf{1}.9 \\ \hline \mathbf{5}.5 \end{array}$

Try These

Estimate each sum.

1. **a)** $2.8 + 3.4$ **b)** $5.9 + 2.8$ **c)** $4.3 + 5.2$

   _5.9_   _8.7_   _9.5_

2. Add. Use Base Ten Blocks to help you.

   a) $3.2 + 4.5 =$ _7.7_   **b)** $6.6 + 2.4 =$ _9.0_   **c)** $3.5 + 8.7 =$ _12.2_

Practice

1. Add. Use Base Ten Blocks or pictures of the blocks to help you.

   a) $1.7 + 4.9 =$ _____   b) $6.5 + 2.7 =$ _____   c) $3.9 + 8.6 =$ _____

   d) $3.8 + 2.7 =$ _____   e) $2.4 + 6.3 =$ _____   f) $4.1 + 6.4 =$ _____

2. Use place value to find each sum.

   a) $\begin{array}{r} 4.2 \\ +\,2.3 \\ \hline \end{array}$ b) $\begin{array}{r} 1.7 \\ +\,5.6 \\ \hline \end{array}$ c) $\begin{array}{r} 7.3 \\ +\,2.8 \\ \hline \end{array}$ d) $\begin{array}{r} 2.3 \\ +\,1.6 \\ \hline \end{array}$ e) $\begin{array}{r} 6.4 \\ +\,9.7 \\ \hline \end{array}$

   f) $\begin{array}{r} 7.4 \\ +\,8.6 \\ \hline \end{array}$ g) $\begin{array}{r} 3.7 \\ +\,1.9 \\ \hline \end{array}$ h) $\begin{array}{r} 8.2 \\ +\,3.8 \\ \hline \end{array}$ i) $\begin{array}{r} 5.7 \\ +\,6.7 \\ \hline \end{array}$ j) $\begin{array}{r} 3.2 \\ +\,9.8 \\ \hline \end{array}$

3. Kruti jogged 2.8 km on Saturday and 1.9 km on Sunday. How far did she jog altogether?

4. Alexander grew two pumpkins in his garden. One had a mass of 4.7 kg. The other had a mass of 3.6 kg. What was the total mass of both pumpkins?

Stretch Your Thinking

1. a) Write two decimals whose sum is approximately 5.

   b) Write two decimals whose sum is closer to 1 than 2.

Subtracting Decimals

Quick Review

You can use whole number strategies
to subtract decimals.

➤ Use rounding to estimate 4.2 − 1.7.
The difference of 4.2 and 1.7 is about 2.

> 4.2 is close to 4.
> 1.7 is close to 2.
> 4 − 2 = 2
> So 4.2 − 1.7 is about 2.

➤ Use Base Ten Blocks to subtract.

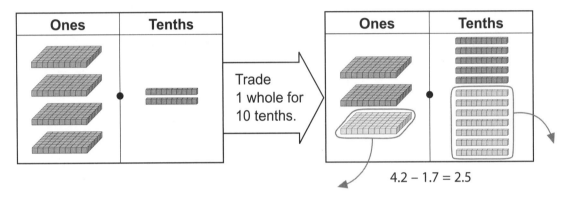

Trade
1 whole for
10 tenths.

4.2 − 1.7 = 2.5

➤ Use place value to subtract. Try to subtract the tenths.

You cannot take 7 tenths from 2 tenths.	Trade 1 whole for 10 tenths.	Subtract the tenths.	Subtract the ones.
4.**2** − 1.**7**	**3 12** $\cancel{4}.\cancel{2}$ − 1.7	**3 12** $\cancel{4}.\cancel{2}$ − 1.**7** .**5**	**3 12** $\cancel{4}.\cancel{2}$ − 1.**7** **2**.5

Try These

1. Estimate each difference.

    a) 5.8 − 2.9   b) 8.1 − 3.2   c) 2.1 − 0.9

    _____   _____   _____

2. Subtract.

    a) 8.4 − 3.2 = _____   b) 7.9 − 4.2 = _____   c) 6.4 − 2.5 = _____

136

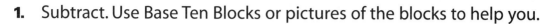

1. Subtract. Use Base Ten Blocks or pictures of the blocks to help you.

   a) 7.4 – 2.3 = _____   b) 2.7 – 0.8 = _____   c) 4.2 – 3.8 = _____

   d) 4.9 – 2.6 = _____   e) 5.2 – 3.7 = _____   f) 0.9 – 0.2 = _____

2. Use place value to find each difference.

   a)   9.3   b)   10.2   c)   14.8   d)   8.5   e)   6.4
      – 6.4   – 3.6   – 6.9   – 0.7   – 2.8

   f)   8.4   g)   3.8   h)   7.5   i)   12.6   j)   10.4
      – 0.9   – 1.2   – 2.8   – 9.9   – 3.7

3. When Baily planted a new evergreen tree it was 1.3 m tall.
   Now it is 2.1 m tall.

   How much has it grown? _____

4. Symron lives 2.4 km from the movie theatre.
   Sofia lives 3.1 km from the theatre.

   How much further away does Sofia live? _____

Stretch Your Thinking

1. a) Name two decimals whose difference is approximately 2.

   _____

   b) Name two decimals whose difference is between 2 and 3, but closer to 3.

   _____

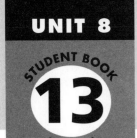

UNIT 8
STUDENT BOOK 13 LESSON

Adding and Subtracting Money

At Home At School

Quick Review

You can use different methods to add and subtract money amounts.

➤ You can use a place-value mat.

➤ You can count on.

➤ You can use place value.
What is the change from $5 when you spend $3.52?
Use place value and subtraction to find out.

Line up the decimal points.	Trade $1 for 10 dimes. Trade 1 dime for 10 pennies.	Subtract the cents.	Subtract the dollars.
	9 4 10̸ 10	4 9 10	4 9 10
$ 5.00 – 3.52	$ 5̸.0̸0̸ – 3.52	$ 5̸.0̸0̸ – 3.**52** .**48**	$ 5̸.0̸0̸ – 3.52 **1.48**

The change from $5 is $1.48.

Try These

1. Add or subtract.

   a) $2.49
   +1.30

   b) $4.26
   +3.49

   c) $9.32
   – 4.50

   d) $7.27
   – 4.88

2. Find each sum or difference.

   a) $5.39 + $2.20 = _____

   b) $1.49 + $7.37 = _____

   c) $14.55 – $8.32 = _____

   d) $10.00 – $8.23 = _____

1. Find each sum.
   a) $6.70
      + 2.85
      9.55

   b) $2.57
      + 5.84
      8.41

   c) $6.85
      + 1.78
      8.62

   d) $1.99
      + 0.67
      2.66

2. Find each difference.
   a) $6.74
      − 2.54

   b) $5.75
      − 2.83
      3.12

   c) $7.00
      − 2.51
      5.00

   d) $3.49
      − 0.58
      0.11

3. Use the prices in the table to solve
   the problems.

   Beach Supplies

Sun Hat	$5.79
Sunglasses	$8.95
Beach Towel	$9.85
Beach Ball	$1.59
Flippers	$4.67
Sun Umbrella	$12.84

   a) Yvonne bought a sun hat and
      beach towel.
      How much did she spend?

   _____

   b) How much change did Yvonne

      get from $20? _____

   c) Sandy bought two items. She spent $13.62.
      Which two items did she buy?

   _____

   d) How much more does a sun umbrella cost than a beach towel? _____

Stretch Your Thinking

Malio bought two items from the Beach Supplies table.
He got $2.62 change from $10.

Which two items did he buy? _____

_____

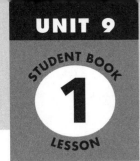
Measuring Linear Dimensions

Quick Review

Length, width, height, thickness, and depth are linear dimensions.

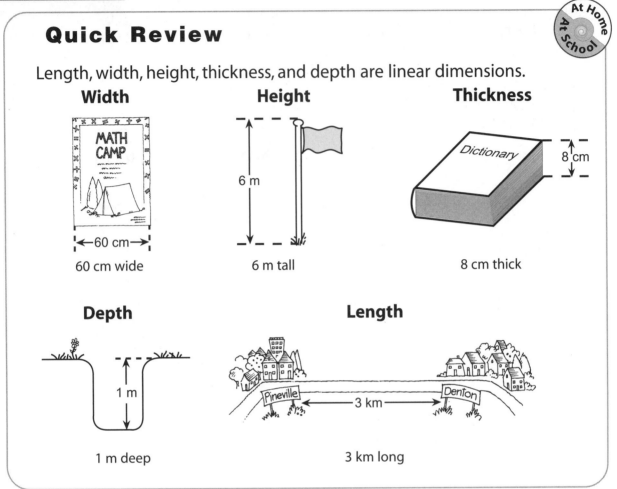

Width

MATH CAMP

←60 cm→

60 cm wide

Height

6 m

6 m tall

Thickness

Dictionary

8 cm

8 cm thick

Depth

1 m

1 m deep

Length

Pineville ←3 km→ Denton

3 km long

Try These

1. Measure each item to the nearest centimetre or metre.

   a) the height of your desk _____

   b) the length of your teacher's desk _____

   c) the width of your thumb _____

   d) the thickness of a blackboard eraser _____

1. Find an object that fits each description.
   Measure to the nearest centimetre or metre.
   Complete the chart.

Description	Object	Measure
About 2 m long		
Taller than you		
About 20 cm wide		
Thicker than 1 cm		
About 15 cm deep		

Stretch Your Thinking ·

Draw a rectangle that is 6 cm × 2 cm.
Label its linear dimensions.

Measuring in Millimetres

At Home
At School

Quick Review

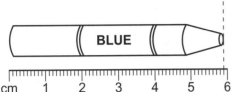
BLUE

cm   1   2   3   4   5   6

You can read the length of this crayon to the nearest centimetre.
The crayon is about 6 cm long.

To be more precise, you can read the length in millimetres.
The crayon is 59 mm long.

One millimetre is one-tenth of a centimetre.

So, you can say the length in centimetres.
The crayon is 5.9 cm long.

You say: 5 and 9 tenths centimetres

10 mm = 1 cm
So, 1 mm = 0.1 cm

Try These

1. Estimate the length of each line to the nearest centimetre.
   Then, measure and record the actual length in millimetres and centimetres.

	Estimate (cm)	Length (mm)	Length (cm)
a)			
b)			
c)			

1. Work with a partner.

    You will need:
    Small objects, such as a pencil, a crayon, a paper clip, a straw, a craft stick
    A 30-cm ruler

    ➤ Choose an object.
    ➤ Both of you estimate the object's length to the nearest centimetre.
    ➤ Record your estimates.
    ➤ Measure and record the actual length in millimetres and in centimetres.
    ➤ Repeat with other objects.

Object	Our Estimates (cm)	Actual Length (mm)	Actual Length (cm)
Pencil			
Crayon			
Paper Clip			
Straw			
Craft stick			

Stretch Your Thinking

Measure and record the width of your hand and your foot.
Complete the chart.

	Width (mm)	Width (cm)
Hand		
Foot		
Difference		

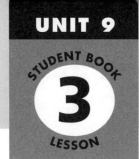
Measuring in Decimetres

Quick Review

A decimetre is the same length as 10 centimetres.
A Base Ten rod is 1 decimetre long.
An orange Cuisenaire rod is 1 decimetre long.

The flower is 200 mm tall.

The flower is 20 cm tall.

The flower is 2 dm tall.

| 1 dm = 10 cm |
| 1 dm = 100 mm |

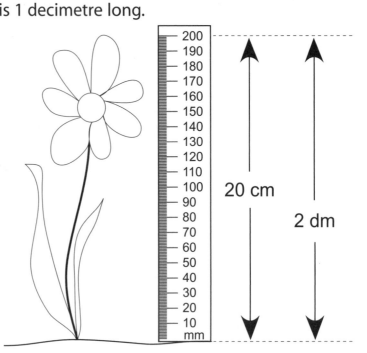

Try These

1. Use Base Ten rods or orange Cuisenaire rods. Measure each item to the nearest decimetre.

   a) the width of your desk _____

   b) the width of your math book _____

   c) the length of a bookcase _____

   d) the width of the classroom door _____

   e) the length of this page _____

Use a metre stick to help you.

1. Complete.

   a) 50 dm = _2_ cm   **b)** 35 dm = _2 ˀ_ cm   **c)** 15 dm = _____ cm

   d) 50 cm = _20_ dm   **e)** 20 cm = _____ dm   **f)** 90 cm = _____ dm

2. Which is longer?
   a) 22 cm or 2 dm   **b)** 500 mm or 7 dm   **c)** 36 cm or 300 mm

   _____   _____   _____

3. Play this game with a partner.

   You will need:
   Index cards
   Paper to keep track of your points
   Metre stick

   How to play:

   ➤ Make two sets of cards. Label cards in one set:
      1, 2, 3, 4, 5, 6, 7, 8, 9, and 10 dm.
      Label cards in the other set 10, 20, 30, 40, 50, 60, 70, 80, 90, and 100 cm.
      Shuffle each set.
   ➤ Give one partner the decimetre set and the other partner the centimetre set.
   ➤ Each player takes a card from the top of the set.
   ➤ Compare the lengths that come up. Use a metre stick to help you.
   ➤ The player with the longer length gets a point.
   ➤ If the lengths are equal, no one gets a point.
   ➤ Continue until one player has 10 points.

Stretch Your Thinking ·

Play the game again. This time the player with the longer length gets an extra
point for naming the length in millimetres.

Relating Units of Measure

Quick Review

One metre equals 100 cm.

So, 1 cm is $\frac{1}{100}$ of a metre, or 0.01 m.

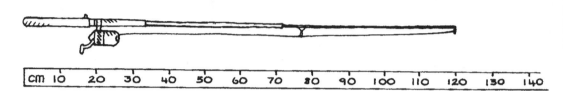

| cm 10 | 20 | 30 | 40 | 50 | 60 | 70 | 80 | 90 | 100 | 110 | 120 | 130 | 140 |

You can write the length of the fishing pole as:

| 120 cm | or | 1 m 20 cm | or | 1.20 m | or | 12 dm |

Remember these.

1 m = 10 dm	**1 dm = 10 cm**	**1 cm = 10 mm**	**1 mm = 0.1 cm**
1 m = 100 cm	**1 dm = 100 mm**	**1 cm = 0.01 m**	
1 m = 1000 mm		**10 cm = 0.1 m**	

Try These ·

Complete.

1. a) 5 m = _____ cm   **b)** 0.50 m = _____ cm

    c) 140 cm = _____ m   **d)** 60 cm = _____ m

2. a) 1 dm = _____ cm   **b)** 70 dm = _____ cm

    c) 30 cm = _____ dm   **d)** 3 cm = _____ dm

3. a) 70 cm = _____ mm   **b)** 18 cm = _____ mm

    c) 40 mm = _____ cm   **d)** 43 mm = _____ cm

1. Look around the room to find the items pictured in the chart.
   Estimate the measurement of each item to the nearest centimetre.
   Measure and record the measurements.

Object	Estimate (cm)	Length (cm)	Length (mm)	Length (m)

Stretch Your Thinking

Cut off a piece of string any length. Measure the string.
Record its length in as many ways as you can.

Measuring Perimeter

Quick Review

The distance around an object or figure is its **perimeter**.

Find the perimeter of an object by measuring the lengths of its sides and then adding the lengths together.

Perimeter = 4 cm + 3.4 cm + 4 cm + 3.4 cm
Perimeter = 14.8 cm

When the side lengths are given, add to find the perimeter. This figure is drawn to **scale**. That is, each side represents the given length.

Perimeter = 25 cm + 25 cm + 15 cm
Perimeter = 65 cm

Try These

1. Find the perimeter of each object or figure.

a)

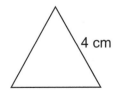

15 cm

7 cm · · · 7 cm

15 cm

Perimeter = _____

b)

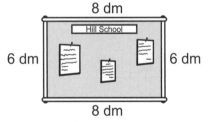

8 dm

6 dm · · · 6 dm

8 dm

Perimeter = _____

c)

4 cm

Perimeter = _____

d)

2 cm

6 cm

Perimeter = _____

1. Find objects to fit each description.
   Complete the chart.

Description	Object	Actual Perimeter
Perimeter between 50 and 80 cm		
Perimeter between 100 and 200 mm		
Perimeter greater than 15 dm		
Perimeter less than 20 cm		
Perimeter between 10 and 20 dm		
Perimeter less than 1 m		
Perimeter about 50 cm		

Stretch Your Thinking ·

The perimeter of an isosceles triangle is 30 cm.
How long might its sides be?
Give two different answers.
Explain.

_____

_____

_____

Finding the Perimeter of a Large Region

Quick Review

To measure the perimeter of a large region, use metres or kilometres as the unit of length.

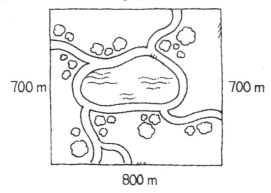

800 m

700 m   700 m

800 m

Lincoln Pond Park

The perimeter of this park = 800 m + 700 m + 800 m + 700 m = 3000 m

Since 1000 m = 1 km, then 3000 m = 3 km

The perimeter of the park is 3 km.

1 km = 1000 m

Try These

1. Complete.

   a) 2000 m = _____ km   **b)** 9000 m = _____ km   **c)** 5000 m = _____ km

   d) 7 km = _____ m   **e)** 4 km = _____ m   **f)** 10 km = _____ m

2. Find the perimeter of each region.

   a)   **b)**

   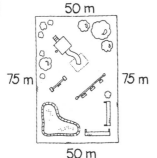

   50 m

   75 m   75 m

   50 m

   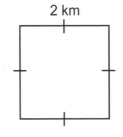

   2 km

   We use hatch marks to show equal sides.

   Perimeter = _____   Perimeter = _____

150

1. Find the perimeter of each figure.

a)

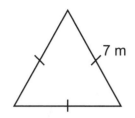

Perimeter = _____

b)

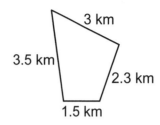

Perimeter = _____

2. Label the lengths of the sides of each square.

a)

Perimeter = 8 km

b)

Perimeter = 2 km

3. Number the figures in order from least to greatest perimeter.

a)

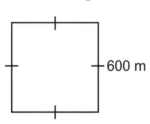

_____

b)

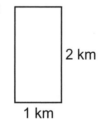

_____

c)

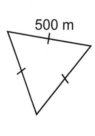

_____

Suppose you bought 16 m of fencing to put around your rectangular garden.
What dimensions might your garden be?
Give two different answers.

_____

_____

Exploring Area

Quick Review

To find the **area** of a figure, count the number of square units
needed to cover it.

The area of this figure
is 5 square units.

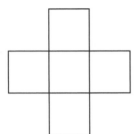

To find the area of a rectangle,
you can count the number of
square units or you can multiply.
There are 2 rows of 5 squares.
$2 \times 5 = 10$
The area of this rectangle
is 10 square units.

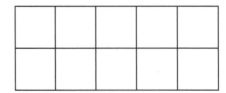

Try These . . . .

1. Find the area of each figure in square units.

   a)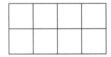

   b)

   c)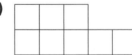

   _____ square units   _____ square units   _____ square units

2. Write a multiplication sentence to find the area of each rectangle.

   a)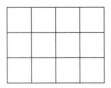

   b)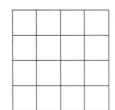

   c)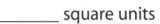

Practice

1. Play this game with a partner.

   You will need:
   2 number cubes   2 pencil crayons of different colours

   Take turns:
   - Roll the cubes. Add the numbers to get an area in square units.
   - Colour a figure with that area on the grid.
   - No figure can overlap another figure.
   - If there is no room left for your figure, lose your turn.
   - Continue until there is no more room on the grid.

Stretch Your Thinking

Find the total area you coloured on the grid. Then find the total area your partner coloured. Who coloured the greater area?

____

____

____

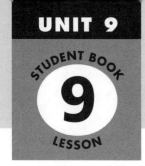
Measuring Area in Square Centimetres

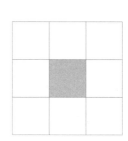

Quick Review

Each side of every square on this grid paper is 1 cm long.

Every square has an area of one **square centimetre** (1 cm^2).

You can use square centimetres to measure area.

At Home At School

Try These

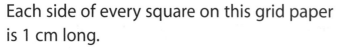

1. Find the area of each figure in square centimetres.

a)

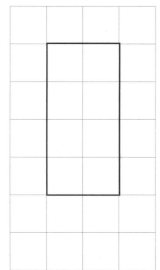

Area = _____

b)

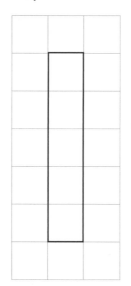

Area = _____

c)

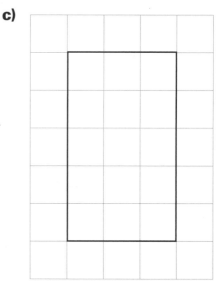

Area = _____

1. Write the area inside each figure in square centimetres.

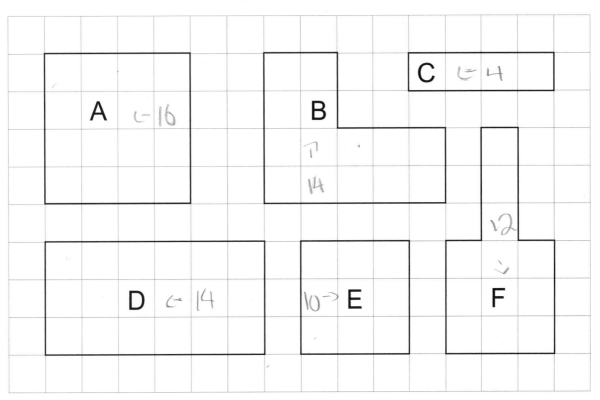

A ← 16
B ⊓ 14
C ← 4
D ← 14
10 → E
F ∨2

2. Draw three different rectangles with area 12 cm².

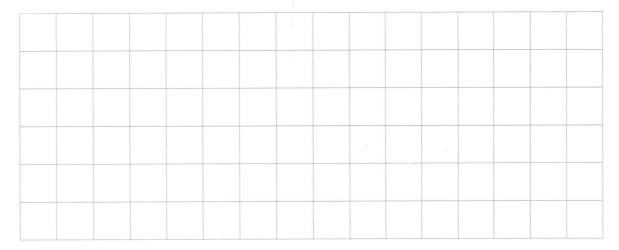

Stretch Your Thinking

The area of a square is 25 cm². What are its linear dimensions?

Estimating and Measuring Area

Quick Review

This is one way to find the approximate area of a triangle.

➤ Count each whole square.
There are 8 whole squares.

➤ Count each half square.
There are 4 half squares.
This equals 2 whole squares.

➤ Count each part greater than $\frac{1}{2}$ a square as 1 square.
There are 2 parts greater than $\frac{1}{2}$ a square.

➤ Ignore each part less than $\frac{1}{2}$ a square.

➤ Add to find the total number of squares: $8 + 2 + 2 = 12$

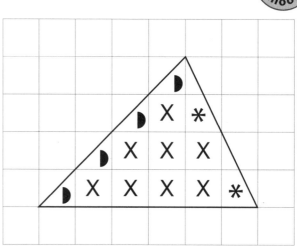

This triangle has an area of about 12 cm².

Try These

1. Find the approximate area of each figure.

a)

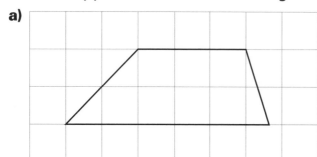

Area = about _____

b)

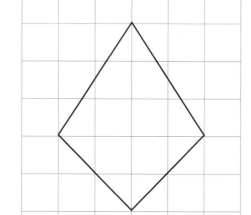

Area = about _____

1. Draw a large clown's head on the grid. Use as many different polygons as you can. Find the approximate area of each part of the head.

	Nose	**Mouth**	**One Eye**	**Whole Head**
Approximate Area				

Stretch Your Thinking . . . .

Explain how you would find the approximate area of a leaf.

_____

_____

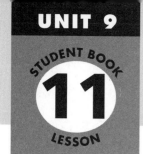

Finding Area in Square Metres

Quick Review

At Home
At School

A square with side lengths of 1 m has an area of one **square metre** ($1 m^2$).

You can use grid paper to model a large area. Each square represents $1 m^2$.

This is a model of a strawberry patch. It is 7 m wide and 8 m long. The model has 7 rows of 8 squares. $7 \times 8 = 56$

The area of the strawberry patch is $56 m^2$.

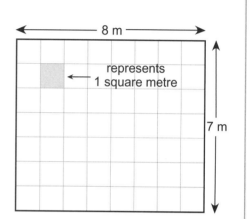

8 m

represents 1 square metre

7 m

Try These

1. Find the area of each garden. Each square has an area of $1 m^2$.

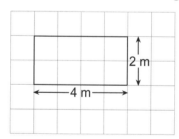

2 m

4 m

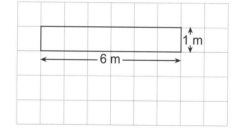

1 m

6 m

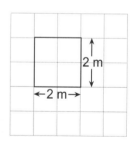

2 m

2 m

a) Area = _____

b) Area = _____

c) Area = _____

2. Put the rectangles in question 1 in order from least to greatest area.

_____

1. Here are the dimensions of each of Sheila's gardens.
Model each of the gardens on the grid.
   ➤ Find the area of each garden.
   ➤ On each model, record the area and the type of flowers.

Sheila's Gardens

Flowers	Width	Length
Roses	7 m	3 m
Wildflowers	5 m	4 m
Pansies	1 m	8 m
Petunias	6 m	4 m
Daisies	10 m	2 m

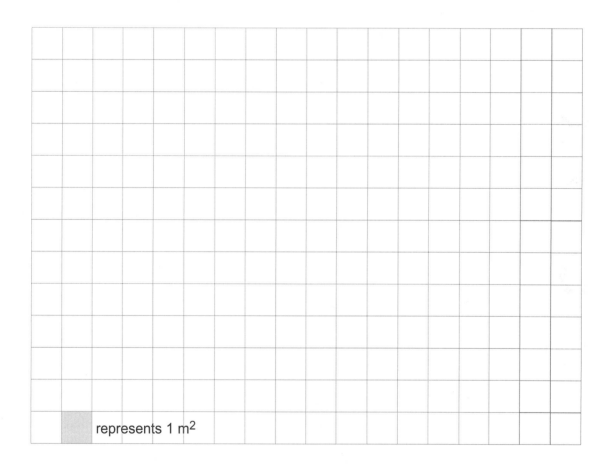

represents 1 m²

Stretch Your Thinking . . . .

Sheila has a rectangular pumpkin patch with area 36 m².
The patch is 4 m wide. How long is it?

_____

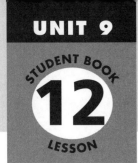
Exploring Figures with Equal Perimeters

Quick Review

Perimeter is the distance around an object.
Figures can have equal perimeters, even if they have different areas.

Each figure has a perimeter of 8 cm.

The square has an area of 4 cm² and the rectangle has an area of 3 cm².

Try This

1. Draw all possible rectangles with a perimeter of 18 cm. Label each rectangle with its area.

= 1 cm²

Find the perimeter and the area of each rectangle.
Then draw another rectangle with the same perimeter.
Record the area of the rectangle you drew.

Each small square has an area of 1 cm².

1.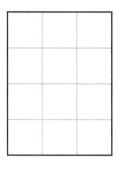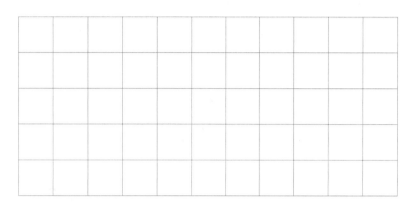

Perimeter = _____

Area = _____   Area = _____

2.

Perimeter = _____   Area = _____

Area = _____

Stretch Your Thinking ·

Suppose the area of your rectangular garden is 5 m².
What is its perimeter? Explain.

_____

_____

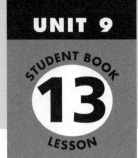
Exploring Figures with Equal Areas

Quick Review

Figures with different perimeters can have equal areas.
Each figure below has a different perimeter, but has an area of 10 m².
The rectangle has a perimeter of 14 m, while the other figure
has a perimeter of 18 m.

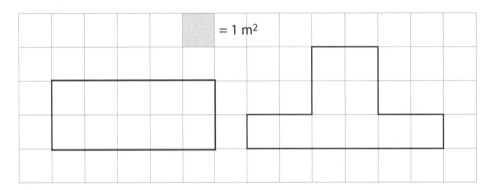

= 1 m²

Try These •

1. Find the area and perimeter of each figure.

a)

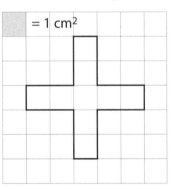

= 1 cm²

b)

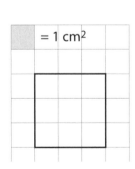

= 1 cm²

c)

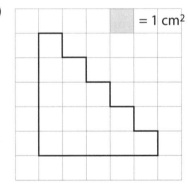

= 1 cm²

Area = _____   Area = _____   Area = _____

Perimeter = _____   Perimeter = _____   Perimeter = _____

d) Which figures have equal areas? _____

1. Work with a partner.

➤ Draw a figure on the grid.
➤ Record the area and the perimeter on the figure.
   Your partner draws a different figure with the same area,
   and records the area and the perimeter.
➤ Switch roles and repeat. Continue the game until the grid is full.

= 1 cm²										

Stretch Your Thinking ⬤

Draw two figures on the grid,
each with an area of 1 cm².

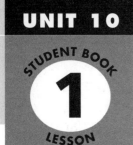

Repeating Patterns

Quick Review

This is a **repeating pattern**.
In this pattern, three attributes
change: size, colour, and shape.

This is the core.

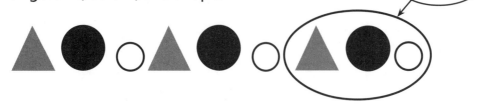

There are 3 figures in the core.
To predict the 20th figure in this pattern, you can count on.
Start at 1 and count on by 3s until you get close to 20.

1, 4, 7, 10, 13, 16, 19

The 19th figure is the same as the 1st figure.
So, the 20th figure is the same as the 2nd figure.

The 20th figure is a large black circle.

Try These . . . .

1. **a)** Predict the 15th figure in this pattern. _____
   b) Extend the pattern to check your prediction.

2. **a)** Predict the 24th coin in this pattern. _____

   b) How many coins would you need in the pattern to show 10 repeats of

   the core? _____

1. a) Draw a repeating pattern of squares in which three attributes change.
Show two repeats of the core.

b) Predict what the 19th figure will be. _____

How did you make your prediction? _____

_____

_____

2. Each of the 15 lockers in the gym has been painted one of four colours.
The core of the pattern is red, blue, yellow, green.

a) What colour is the 14th locker? _____

b) How many lockers of each colour are there?

red _____   blue _____   yellow _____   green _____

3. a) Predict the 19th coin in this pattern. _____

b) Suppose the pattern had 5 repeats of the core.

How much money would the coins be worth? _____

Stretch Your Thinking ·

Georgina made a necklace using 120 beads.
This is the core of her pattern:

What colour is the 87th bead on the necklace? _____

How many black beads did Georgina use? _____

Patterns in Multiplication

Quick Review

You can use multiples of 10 to multiply a 2-digit number by a 1-digit number.

➤ Multiply: 7×89

Think:

89 is 1 less than 90.
So, 7×89 is
7 less than 7×90.
$7 \times 90 = 630$
Subtract 7.
$630 - 7 = 623$
So, $7 \times 89 = 623$

➤ Multiply: 6×52

Think:

52 is 2 more than 50.
So, 6×52 is
6×50 plus 6×2.
$6 \times 50 = 300$
Add 6×2, or 12.
$300 + 12 = 312$
So, $6 \times 52 = 312$

Try These

Multiply. Use multiples of 10 to help you.

1. a) $6 \times 78 =$ _____   b) $4 \times 29 =$ _____   c) $5 \times 59 =$ _____

   d) $7 \times 68 =$ _____   e) $8 \times 27 =$ _____   f) $9 \times 79 =$ _____

2. a) $8 \times 31 =$ _____   b) $7 \times 52 =$ _____   c) $6 \times 42 =$ _____

   d) $4 \times 92 =$ _____   e) $9 \times 71 =$ _____   f) $8 \times 62 =$ _____

3. a) $53 \times 8 =$ _____   b) $79 \times 7 =$ _____   c) $61 \times 6 =$ _____

   d) $82 \times 5 =$ _____   e) $58 \times 4 =$ _____   f) $32 \times 9 =$ _____

1. Use patterns to complete each multiplication chart.

a)

X	12	13	14	15
5				
6				
7				

b)

X	20	21	22	23
7				
8				
9				

2. Hot dogs cost $2. How much do 7 hot dogs cost?

_____

3. Marbles are sold in bags of 49. How many marbles are in 8 bags?

_____

4. There are 52 cards in a deck. How many cards are in 7 decks?

_____

5. There are 13 donuts in a baker's dozen.

   How many donuts are there in 9 bakers' dozens? _____

6. There are 24 pencil-tip erasers in a package.

   How many erasers are there in 6 packages? _____

Stretch Your Thinking

Explain how you could use patterns to find 7 × 699.

_____

_____

_____

Multiplying a 3-Digit Number by a 1-Digit Number

Quick Review

Margaret bought 5 boxes of paper clips.
Each box contains 175 paper clips.
How many paper clips did she get?

The total number of paper clips is 5 × 175.

Here is one way to multiply:
Break 175 apart.
Multiply each part by 5.
Then add.

$$\begin{array}{r} 175 \\ \times\ 5 \end{array}$$

Multiply the ones: 5 × 5 ⟶ 25
Multiply the tens: 5 × 70 ⟶ 350
Multiply the hundreds: 5 × 100 ⟶ + 500
Add.

$$875$$

Margaret got 875 paper clips.

Try These ·

1. Multiply.

   a) 340
   × 2

   b) 121
   × 9

   c) 517
   × 8

   d) 258
   × 7

   e) 409
   × 6

2. Lester has 3 books of stickers. Each book has 144 stickers.

   How many stickers does Lester have? _____

1. Multiply.

   a) 763   b) 495   c) 508   d) 659   e) 828
      × 4   × 8   × 9   × 5   × 3

2. There are 125 balloons in a bag.
   How many balloons are there in 7 bags? _____

3. Play this game with a partner.
   You will need a set of 10 cards numbered 0 to 9.
   ➤ Each of you draw a multiplication grid like this:

   ➤ Shuffle the cards and lay them face side down.
   ➤ Take turns flipping over a card.
      Each time a card is turned over, both players
      write that number in any box on their grids.
   ➤ Continue until players have filled all the
      boxes on their grids.
   ➤ Multiply. The player with the greater product wins.
   Play 5 more games.

Stretch Your Thinking

Choose a 3-digit number to multiply by 8 so that the
product is between 4000 and 5000, but closer to 4000.

Growing Patterns

Quick Review

Here is a **growing pattern** with squares.

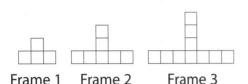

Frame 1   Frame 2   Frame 3

Frames	Squares Added	Squares in a Frame
1	—	4
2	3	7
3	3	10

➤ Each frame has 3 more squares than the frame before.
You can record this pattern in a table.
Each time, 3 squares are added.
Add 3 squares to Frame 3 to make Frame 4.

➤ The pattern rule for the number of squares in a frame is:
Start at 4. Add 3 each time.

➤ Extend the pattern to predict the number of squares in Frame 9:
4, 7, 10, 13, 16, 19, 22, 25, 28
There will be 28 squares in Frame 9.

Try These ·

1. Use congruent squares to build
this growing pattern.

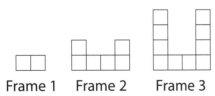

Frame 1   Frame 2   Frame 3

Frames	Squares Added	Squares in a Frame

a) Build Frame 4 and Frame 5.
Complete the table.

b) What is the pattern rule for the number of squares in a frame?

_____

c) How many squares will be needed to build Frame 10? _____

1. Use toothpicks to build this growing pattern.

  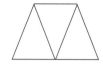

Frame 1   Frame 2   Frame 3

Frame	Toothpicks Added	Toothpicks in a Frame

a) Build the next 3 frames. Complete the table.

b) Write a pattern rule for the number of toothpicks in a frame.

_____

c) Predict the number of toothpicks needed for Frame 15.

_____

2. Here is a growing pattern made with pennies and nickels.

Frame 1   Frame 2   Frame 3

a) Write a pattern rule for the number of pennies and nickels in a frame.

_____

b) How many of each kind of coin do you need to build Frame 10?

_____

c) What sum of money is in Frame 10? _____

Stretch Your Thinking

The pattern rule for the number of buttons in a frame is:
Start at 3. Add 4 each time.
How many buttons will be in Frame 10? _____

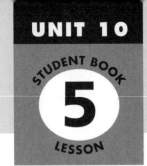
Changing-Step Growing Patterns

Quick Review

> ➤ This is a **same-step growing pattern**.

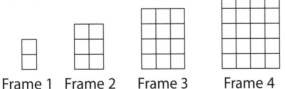

Frame 1   Frame 2   Frame 3

Frame	Blocks Added	Blocks in a Frame
1	—	1
2	3	4
3	3	7

Three blocks are added each time.
The pattern rule for the number of blocks in a frame is: Start at 1. Add 3 each time.

> ➤ This is a **changing-step growing pattern**.

Frame 1   Frame 2   Frame 3   Frame 4

Frame	Blocks Added	Blocks in a Frame
1	—	1
2	5	6
3	9	15
4	13	28

The number of blocks added increases by 4 each time.
The pattern rule for the number of blocks in a frame is:
Start at 1. Add 5. Increase the number you add by 4 each time.

Try These

1. Use congruent squares to build this pattern.

Frame 1   Frame 2   Frame 3   Frame 4

Frames	Squares Added	Squares in a Frame

a) Build Frame 5. Complete the table.

b) What is the pattern rule for the number of squares in a frame?

_____

c) What kind of a pattern is this? _____

1. Look at this pattern.

   Frame 1   Frame 2   Frame 3   Frame 4

Frame	Squares Added	Squares in a Frame

   a) Complete the table for this pattern.

   b) How any squares are needed to build the 8th frame? _____

   c) How did you make your prediction? _____

   _____

2. Look at the pattern in question 1.
   a) Find the perimeter in units of each frame.
      Complete the table.
   b) What will the perimeter of Frame 10 be? _____
   c) How do you know?

Frame	Perimeter

   _____

   _____

3. Use pennies or counters to make four frames
   of a changing-step growing pattern.
   Record your pattern in the table.
   How many pennies would there be in Frame 7?

   _____

Frame	Pennies Added	Pennies in a Frame

Stretch Your Thinking

How many frames of this pattern
could you make with 50 squares?

Frame 1   Frame 2   Frame 3

_____

How many squares would the last frame have? _____

Patterns in Division with Remainders

Quick Review

You can use skip counting to divide.

Divide: $59 \div 7$
Start at 7 and count on by 7s:

    7, 14, 21, 28, 35, 42, 49, 56

There are 8 sevens in 59 and 3 left over.
So, $59 \div 7 = 8\ R3$

Try These

1. Use skip counting to divide.

    a) $37 \div 6 =$ _____ **b)** $38 \div 9 =$ _____ **c)** $15 \div 5 =$ _____ **d)** $25 \div 3 =$ _____

    e) $44 \div 8 =$ _____ **f)** $17 \div 4 =$ _____ **g)** $21 \div 2 =$ _____ **h)** $16 \div 7 =$ _____

2. Divide. Look for patterns.

    a) $30 \div 6 =$ _____ **b)** $29 \div 6 =$ _____ **c)** $28 \div 6 =$ _____ **d)** $27 \div 6 =$ _____

    e) $26 \div 6 =$ _____ **f)** $25 \div 6 =$ _____ **g)** $24 \div 6 =$ _____ **h)** $23 \div 6 =$ _____

    i) What patterns did you find?

    _____

    _____

3. A farmer has 39 hogs. She can fit 6 into each pen.
   How many pens does the farmer need? Explain.

    _____

    _____

1. Play this game with a partner.
    You will need:
    Small counters

    Take turns:

    ➤ Cover any number on the chart with a counter.
    ➤ Choose a number from 2 to 9.
       Divide the number you covered by this number.
    ➤ The remainder is your score. Record your score.
    ➤ Keep playing until all the numbers on the chart are covered.
    ➤ The player with the greater total score wins.

10	11	12	13	14	15	16	17	18
19	20	21	22	23	24	25	26	27
28	29	30	31	32	33	34	35	36
37	38	39	40	41	42	43	44	45
46	47	48	49	50	51	52	53	54
55	56	57	58	59	60	61	62	63
64	65	66	67	68	69	70	71	72
73	74	75	76	77	78	79	80	81

Stretch Your Thinking

Describe the strategy you used to try to win this game.

_____

_____

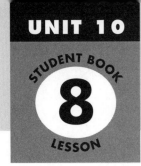
Dividing a 3-Digit Number by a 1-Digit Number

Quick Review

To divide 158 by 4, you can subtract multiples of 4.

Choose any multiple of 4 less than 158. Start with 40.

Subtract 40 from 158.	Then subtract 80.	Then subtract 36.	Add the side numbers.
$4\overline{)158}$ $\underline{-40}$ 10 118	$4\overline{)158}$ $\underline{-40}$ 10 118 $\underline{-80}$ 20 38	$4\overline{)158}$ $\underline{-40}$ 10 118 $\underline{-80}$ 20 38 $\underline{-36}$ 9 2	$4\overline{)158}$ $\underline{-40}$ 10 118 $\underline{-80}$ 20 38 $\underline{-36}$ 9 2

$4\overline{)158}$ is 39 with 2 left over.

$10 + 20 + 9 = 39$

Try These

1. Divide. Show your work.

   a) $3\overline{)246}$ b) $5\overline{)187}$ c) $4\overline{)861}$ d) $6\overline{)358}$

1. Divide.

    a) 467 ÷ 3 = _____   **b)** 184 ÷ 8 = _____   **c)** 462 ÷ 9 = _____

2. Play this game with a partner.
You will need:
1 Base Ten unit cube or other small object

   ➤ Both players draw a division grid like this one: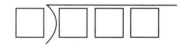

   ➤ Players take turns dropping the
cube onto the numbered circle
with their eyes closed. In any box
on the grids, both players record
the number on which the cube
landed.

   ➤ Continue until all the boxes on
the grids are full.

   ➤ Divide.
The player with the greater answer wins.
Play 5 more games.

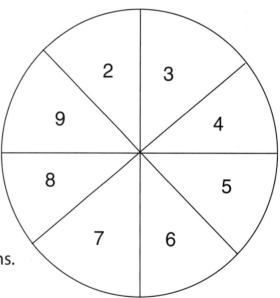

Suppose you are playing the game above.
Where on your grid should you record a 9? Explain.

_____

_____

Area Patterns

Quick Review

Aaron is making this wall hanging
for his bedroom.
The figures in the wall hanging form
an **area pattern**.

There are white squares.
There are white triangles and black triangles.
Four triangles fit the same space as one white square.

How many of each figure will there be in the completed pattern?

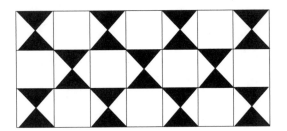

Here is the completed pattern.
There are 10 white squares,
22 white triangles,
and 22 black triangles
in the completed pattern.

Try These

1. Carl is covering a tabletop with tiles.
   The table is square-shaped.
   He continues this pattern.
   Complete the pattern.

2. How many of each tile does
   Carl need to cover the table?

   _____

   _____

1. Extend this pattern.

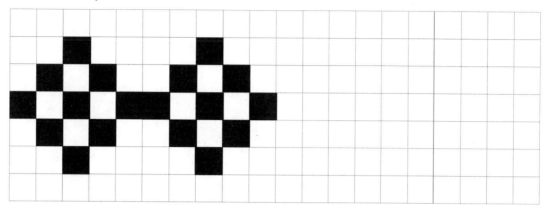

How many squares of each colour will the finished pattern have?

_____

2. Colour an area pattern on this grid.

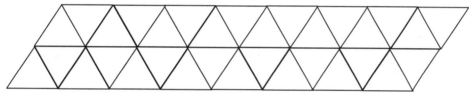

Describe the pattern you made.

_____

_____

_____

_____

Stretch Your Thinking

Make an area pattern with squares or Pattern Blocks. Describe your pattern.
Give your description to a classmate or family member.
Challenge him or her to model your pattern.

_____

_____

_____

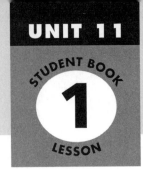
The Language of Probability

Quick Review

Some events are **impossible**.

Some events are **certain**.

Something that is likely to happen is **probable**.
Something that is unlikely to happen is **improbable**.

You can use a line to show how likely it is an event will happen.

←—— unlikely ——→ ←—— likely ——→

impossible ←———————— possible ————————→ certain

Try These

1. Use a word from the box to describe each event.

   a) It will rain meatballs this summer. _____

   b) We will have a fire drill this week.

   _____

   c) You will walk on the moon. _____

   | possible |
   | impossible |
   | certain |
   | unlikely |
   | likely |

2. Colour the spinner so that the
   chances of spinning red and green
   are not equally likely.

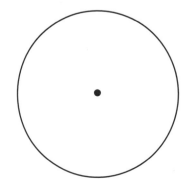

1. Write a sentence using each word.

   a) likely _____

   b) unlikely _____

2. Suppose you spin this pointer.
   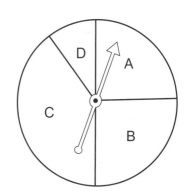
   a) Which letter is the pointer least likely

   to stop on? _____
   b) Which letter is it impossible to stop on?

   _____

   c) Which two letters is it equally likely

   to stop on? _____

3. Suppose you put these cards in a bag and
   then pull one card out without looking.
   Tell which number:

7	2	7
3	7	3
7	3	7

   a) You are least likely to pick. _____

   b) You are most likely to pick. _____
   c) It is impossible to pick.

   _____

Stretch Your Thinking

Suppose your brother says, "I'll spin the pointer.
If I land on an odd number, I'll do the dishes.
If I land on an even number, you'll do the dishes."
Should you take his offer? Explain.

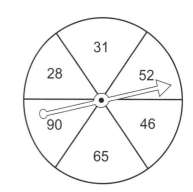

_____

_____

_____

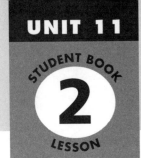
Identifying Outcomes and Predicting Results

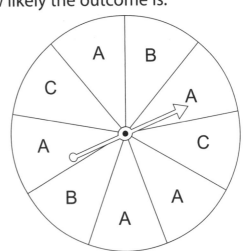

Quick Review

You make a **prediction** when you decide the likelihood of an event.
Spinning the pointer on a spinner to get an **outcome** is an **experiment**.
The **probability** of an outcome is how likely the outcome is.

This spinner has 9 equal sectors.
There are 9 possible outcomes,
but only 3 different outcomes.
Five sectors show A.
The probability of A is 5 out of 9.
You write this as a fraction: $\frac{5}{9}$
The probability of B is 2 out of 9.
You write: $\frac{2}{9}$
The probability of C is 2 out 9.
You write: $\frac{2}{9}$
A is **most probable**. B and C are **equally probable**.

Try These

1. List the possible outcomes for each experiment.
   a) tossing a counter that is yellow on one side and red on the other

   _____

   b) rolling a cube labelled with 2 to 7 dots

   _____

2. Choose words from the box to complete the line
   showing probabilities.

   | less probable |
   | more probable |

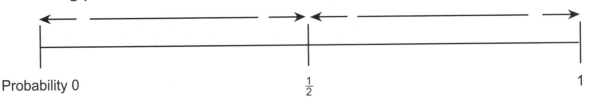

Probability 0 $\frac{1}{2}$ 1

1. Suppose this pointer is spun.

   a) List the possible outcomes.

   _____

   b) How many different outcomes are there?

   _____

   c) What is the probability of the pointer landing on each number?

   _____

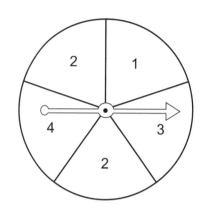

2. Design a spinner so that:
   ➤ Landing on brown is most probable.
   ➤ Landing on orange and landing on green are equally probable.
   ➤ Landing on black is impossible.

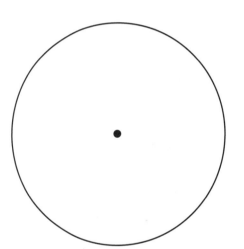

3. Draw 8 squares in the bag so that:
   ➤ Picking a red square is most probable.
   ➤ Picking a yellow square is least probable.
   ➤ Picking a green square and picking an orange square are equally probable.
   ➤ Picking a pink square is impossible.

Stretch Your Thinking

Suppose you roll a cube labelled A, B, D, C, A, D.
Use a fraction to describe the probability of rolling each different outcome.

_____

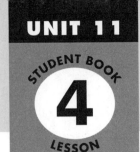
Exploring Predictions

Quick Review

At Home
At School

Inga and Ralph conducted an experiment.
Inga put 4 green cubes and 11 yellow cubes in a bag.
She told Ralph there were 15 cubes in the bag.

Ralph picked a cube, recorded its colour,
then returned the cube to the bag.
He repeated the experiment until he had
the results of 30 trials.

Here are the results.

Green	Yellow
ℋℋ ℋℋ	ℋℋ ℋℋ ℋℋ ℋℋ

The results suggest that there are about two times as many yellow cubes as green cubes. So, Ralph predicts 5 green cubes and 10 yellow cubes.

Try These

1. Suppose Inga put 12 cubes of 2 colours in the bag, and Ralph got these results from 20 trials. What prediction might Ralph make?

Red	White
ℋℋ	ℋℋ ℋℋ ℋℋ

_____

_____

_____

1. **a)** Predict how many times in 40 tosses a bottle cap will land each way:

open side up _____   open side down _____

b) Conduct the experiment.
Record the results on the tally chart.

c) How do your results compare
with your predictions?

Open Side Up	Open Side Down

_____

_____

2. **a)** Look at the spinner below. Predict how many times the pointer
will land on each number in 20 spins.

1: _____   2: _____   3: _____

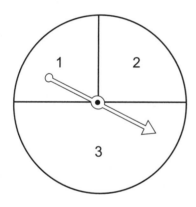

1	
2	
3	

b) Make a copy of the spinner. Use a paper clip and pencil to work the
spinner. Conduct the experiment. Record your results on the tally chart.

c) Explain how your results compare with your predictions.

_____

_____

Stretch Your Thinking

What is the probability of the pointer landing on each number on the

spinner above? _____

Predicted and Actual Results

Quick Review

This spinner has 4 equal parts.
The probability of spinning:

➤ A is 2 out of 4, or $\frac{2}{4}$.

➤ B is 1 out of 4, or $\frac{1}{4}$.

➤ C is 1 out of 4, or $\frac{1}{4}$.

Gabriel will spin the pointer 20 times.

Since $\frac{1}{2}$ of the spinner is labelled A,
Gabriel predicts A will come up 10 times.
Since $\frac{1}{4}$ of the spinner is labelled B and another $\frac{1}{4}$ is labelled C,
Gabriel predicts B and C will each come up 5 times.

Gabriel spins the pointer 20 times.
His results are close to his predictions.

A	B	C
⊬⊬⊬ ⊬⊬⊬ //	⊬⊬⊬	///

Gabriel and 3 classmates combine
their results for a total of 60 spins.
Gabriel predicts A should show 30 times, B 15 times, and C 15 times.
Here are the combined results: A: 29 times; B: 16 times; C: 15 times
The more trials conducted, the closer the **predicted results** are to the
actual results.

Try These

1. Suppose you spin this pointer 40 times.
   a) Predict how many times each number will come up.

      1: _____   2: _____   3: _____

   b) What is the probability each number will come up?

      1: _____   2: _____   3: _____

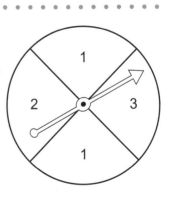

1. Look at each spinner. Predict how many times you would spin a star in 120 spins.

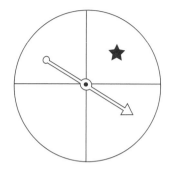 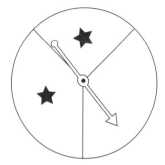 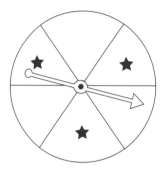

_____   _____   _____

2. Draw a spinner that corresponds to these predicted results of 100 spins.

Red	Green
50	25
Blue	**Orange**
12	13

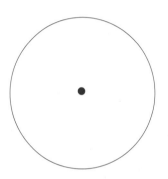

3. What is the probability of spinning a B on each spinner?

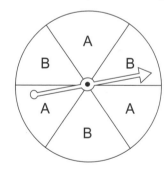 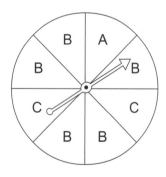 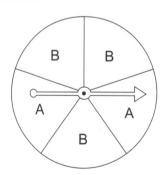

_____   _____   _____

Stretch Your Thinking

Suppose you roll two number cubes that each have the numbers 1 to 6.
Add the numbers that come up.
What are the different outcomes?

_____

Calendar Puzzles

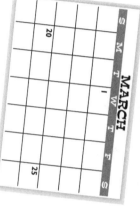

Game

MARCH

S	M	T	W	T	F	S
		1				
20						25

Take a month from an old calendar. Cut out all the squares except the 1st and put them in a paper bag. Now, you can challenge a friend to help you put the month back together!

▼ Pull a square out of the bag. In your head, figure out where that day would lay using the first day as your starting point.

▼ Did you use a pattern to help? Share it with your partner!

▼ Take turns until the month is back in "tiptop" shape! Could you use the same pattern for another month?

Stretchy Shapes

Get a large elastic band and lay it on the table. Put both thumbs and index fingers into the elastic to stretch it out.

Move your fingers in different ways to show quadrilaterals with lots of different attributes. See if someone in your family can guess what they're called!

The next 4 pages fold in half to make an 8-page booklet.

Fold

Math at Home

Math makes lots of sense to me
Until my brain goes numb.
But when I get confused,
I remember the "rule of thumb."

I think about the problem
As it happens day by day.
I grab some stuff and act it out,
Draw it a different way.

Once I've got the picture,
It's time to make a plan.
Now I'm ready to tackle it,
'Cause now I know I can!

Math at Home 1

Sum It Up!

You'll need:

➤ 3 sets of cards numbered 1–9 (shuffled well)

➤ a coin

➤ a large book to use as a barrier

To begin:

Without peeking, each player draws 8 cards and lays them out one at a time, left to right in 2 rows of 4.

Flip the coin.

 Switch the position of 2 cards.   Switch the position of 4 cards.

➤ Both players may switch any 2 or 4 cards to make the largest sum.

So, if you drew this: 1 7 4 8   Then flipped tails …
                    2 9 3 6

You'd probably   8 7 4 1   Switch the 8 and 1.
change it to this: 9 2 3 6   Switch the 9 and 2.

➤ Figure out the sum of your two numbers.

➤ Show your numbers to each other.

➤ The person with the highest sum earns a point.

➤ If the sums are within 1000 of each other, you both earn a point.

➤ The first player with 10 points wins!

On a trip …

Do you find long car rides boring? Watch for a sign showing the number of kilometres to 2 or 3 places.

➤ Can you estimate the distance between those places, before you drive past?

➤ Get everyone in on it. Who can make the best estimate?

(Don't give up! The more you try it, the faster you'll get!)

Belleville	190 km
Kingston	260 km
Brockville	340 km

Secret Shapes

Have someone in your family hide their eyes as you draw any quadrilateral on a piece of paper.

➤ Without uncovering your figure, describe it giving only 3 clues. (Remember attributes such as angles, length of sides, and parallel lines.)

➤ Challenge your partner to draw the figure.

➤ Uncover the one you drew and compare them. Are they close?

➤ Switch places and try again. Do you think the figure will become more similar as you keep trying? Why?

How many?

Oh, no! I was on my way to pick up balls for a "Family Fun Day" when I accidentally spilled pop on my list.

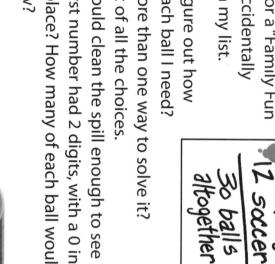

tennis
sponge
12 soccer
30 balls altogether

▶ Can you figure out how many of each ball I need?

▶ Is there more than one way to solve it? Make a list of all the choices.

▶ What if I could clean the spill enough to see that the first number had 2 digits, with a 0 in the ones place? How many of each ball would I need now?

Calculator Patterns 🏃 Game

Enter a number in a calculator and show it to a friend. Secretly, either add or subtract a one-digit number from the first number and press the equal key.

Give the calculator to your friend and ask him to press the equal key 3 more times, watching the numbers change each time. Challenge him to try to figure out what you did!

Switch places and play again!

Art Attack!

Create an abstract sculpture using many 3-D objects, some tape, and your imagination.

First, collect several empty boxes, toilet paper rolls, milk cartons, juice boxes, ice-cream cones, and any other interesting 3-D objects you can find.

Think about how the shapes might fit together and then start taping. Each time you pick up a new object, count the faces and name them.

When you're all done, tell someone about your masterpiece. (Be sure to point out lots of cool "attributes"!)

Crazy Clocks

What time could it be if the minute hand and the hour hand made a right angle? Less than a right angle? More? Is there more than one choice? Use a real clock to find out!

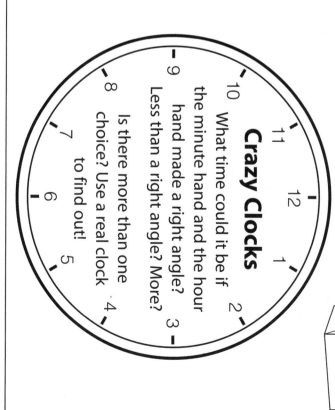

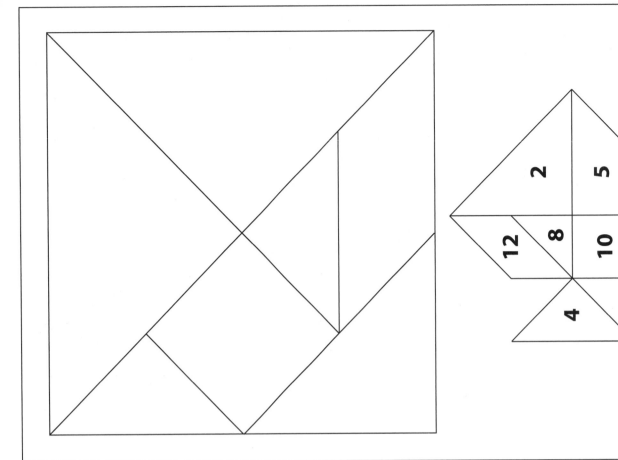

Terrific Tangrams

You'll need:

▲ 3 number cubes

▲ 1 set of tangram pieces for each player (trace the pieces on the next page and cut apart)

The goal here is to earn each piece in order to make the fish on the next page!

On your turn:

▲ Roll all three number cubes.

▲ Add, subtract, multiply, or divide the numbers to try to get an answer that matches a number on a tangram shape.

If you rolled: [1] [3] [5]

You might say, "5 x 1 is 5, and 5 + 3 is 8, so I get the shape with an 8 on it!"

But, there's a catch! Before you can use the piece you earned, you must find something in your house that has at least one angle the same as the tangram piece.

Once you've found a matching angle, begin building the fish by putting the shape in the right spot on the table.

Take turns until someone has got a whole fish!

Pet Survey

16 six-year-olds were surveyed about their favourite pets.

Check the results below!

Dog	Cat	Hamster	Goldfish	Bird
＃＃	///	//	/	/

Now let's make it a bit more interesting!

Take the results from the survey and turn them into a circle graph.

Need a hint?

Figure out what fraction of kids liked each pet best.

Got a minute?

Look at a clock at your house and tell the time in two different ways.

> I guess 1:55 is the same as 5 minutes to 2!

The next 4 pages fold in half to make an 8-page booklet.

Fold

Math at Home

Math is all around my house.
It shows up everywhere.
How many eggs to bake a cake?
How long to brush my hair?

How many strokes will I need
To sweep the upstairs hall?
How many pop star posters
Can I squeeze on my bedroom wall?

How many of my sister's toys
Are scattered on the floor?
Should I pick them up in groups of two
Or grab a whole lot more?

How much water fills the sink
To scrub those dishes clean?
How far can I blow the bubbles
And still keep from being seen?

How many minutes are left
Until all these jobs are done?
But wait! I guess it's no big deal,
'Cause "Mathy" chores are fun!

Multiplication Table for 4-In-A-Row

X	1	2	3	4	5	6	7	8	9
1	1	2	3	4	5	6	7	8	9
2	2	4	6	8	10	12	14	16	18
3	3	6	9	12	15	18	21	24	27
4	4	8	12	16	20	24	28	32	36
5	5	10	15	20	25	30	35	40	45
6	6	12	18	24	30	36	42	48	54
7	7	14	21	28	35	42	49	56	63
8	8	16	24	32	40	48	56	64	72
9	9	18	27	36	45	54	63	72	81

Body Translations

Game

Get a friend to stand facing you. The goal here is to "translate" her from one spot to another. Use words like, "2 steps to the left, 3 steps forward."

(Remember, no rotations!)

Take turns "translating" each other to spots all around the room.

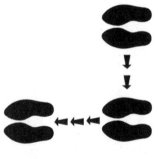

Refrigerator Hunt

Open your fridge and go on a search!

▲ How many containers hold more than a litre?
▲ How many hold less?
▲ Take 3 containers out that hold less than a litre. Look closely at the labels. Read how many millilitres each can hold when full.
▲ Estimate how many millilitres are still left in the container.

Hmmm . . .
How could you check to see if you're right?

4-In-A-Row

Game

You'll need:

▼ different counters for each player

▼ cards numbered 1–10

▼ a multiplication table

On your turn:

▼ Choose 2 cards from the top of the pile.

▼ Find the numbers on the top and side columns of the multiplication chart.

▼ Find the product of the two numbers and put a counter on that square.

▼ If you draw a 10, you get to put your counter on any square.

Take turns until someone gets 4 counters in a row. (The counters can run diagonally, vertically, and horizontally.)

Hey, here's a really cool pattern!

Time Olympics

Game

With a friend, think of 10 "active events" to include in your "Time Olympics."
Print them on separate pieces of paper.

Here are a few ideas to get you started:

▼ Do the "hokey-pokey" 2 times through.

▼ Run around the house 3 times (outside, please!).

▼ Push a cotton ball across the floor with your nose.

▼ Put the pieces of paper face down on the table.

▼ One person chooses one and reads it.

▼ Both players write down an estimate of how long it will take to do the event.

▼ The player who picked the activity begins, while the other person keeps track of the time.

▼ Whoever ends up with the closest estimate keeps the card.

▼ Take turns until all Olympic events are done.

Whoever has the most cards wins GOLD!

Gridlock Gameboard

	A	B	C	D	E	F
6						
5		☆				
4			♡			
3						
2				☺		
1						

♡ Take any counter.

☆ Put 2 counters back on the grid.

☺ Give 1 counter to your opponent.

Gridlock

Game

You'll need:
- ▲ 10 counters
- ▲ a number cube and a letter cube (labelled A–F)

Together, put the 10 counters on the grid.
Don't cover the squares that have pictures.

On your turn:
- ▲ Toss the two cubes.
- ▲ Find the matching square. (Rolling A and 4 describes the square that is 4 rows up in Column A.)
- ▲ If there's a counter on the square, keep it. If there's none, miss your turn.
- ▲ If you land on a picture, check the key below the gameboard for instructions.

The player with the most counters wins!

Quilt Quest

Look closely at the quilt.
How many shapes can you
find that have been rotated,
reflected, or translated.

Hmmm … How many lines of symmetry can you
find? Will there be a lot or just a few?

4

The next 4 pages fold in half to make an 8-page booklet.

At the Mall

▶ Which stores do you think cover the greatest area?

▶ Which ones cover the least?

▶ Which ones are farthest away from each other?

Check the mall layout sign and see if you're right!

Did anything surprise you?

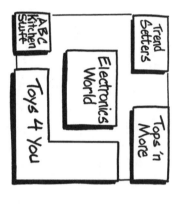

Savvy Saving

If you start with 1¢ and double your savings each day, how long until you have around $5? Guess first, then try it!

How much do you think you'll have by the end of the month? A calculator could be your friend on this one!

Did You Know?

Ralf Laue of Germany can toss a pancake 416 times in 2 minutes. How many times could he do it in 1 minute? 6 minutes? 10 seconds?

Fold

Math at Home

Visiting the supermarket
Needn't make you snore.
Just take a look around
And you'll see Math galore!

Numbers on the labels.
Numbers on the tags.
Numbers on the cash register.
Numbers on the bags.

There are shapes of every size
Lining every aisle.
Angles jumping out at you,
Just browse a little while.

Estimate the grocery bill.
Count up change galore!
But...

Don't ever let me hear you say,
"Shopping's just a BORE!"

RED APPLES 1 kg — $2.99
Orange Juice 300 mL — $1.25
MILK 1L — $1.99
Butter Unsalted 454 g — $4.39
RICE 700 g — $3.79

Math at Home 3

7

How Long? How Wide? How Thick?

 **Game**

You'll need:

▲ 3 of each card — **mm, cm, dm, m**

▲ a number cube

Before you begin, put the cards face down on the table. Decide how many points you'll need to win the game.

On your turn:

▲ Choose a card and roll the number cube.

▲ Find something in your house that is about the same length as the card and number cube show. (If you rolled a 2 and picked a cm card, you'd look for something with a dimension of 2 cm.)

▲ Once you've found something, measure it.

If you're close: 1 point
Exactly right: 2 points

Hmmm … How are you going to decide how close is close enough? Is it harder to guess within 2 mm or 2 m? Why?

Play until one player earns enough points!

String Shapes

Cut two pieces of string 30 cm long. Use one piece to design a dog pen with the greatest possible area. Use the other one to design a pen with the least possible area.

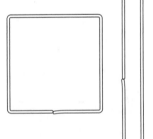

What is the perimeter of both figures? Hmmm … interesting!

Shopping Anyone?

Game

Before you play:

▲ Cut out from a grocery store flyer about 20 items that cost less than $4.00.

▲ Place the pictures in a bag you can't see through.

▲ Each take a pencil and paper and print $20.00 at the top of the page.

On your turn:

▲ Pull a "price tag" out of the bag.

▲ Print the price underneath the $20.00 and subtract. (Estimate first.)

▲ On your next turn, you'll subtract the price from the money you had left from your turn before.

Play until someone runs out of money!

Chocolate Bar Surprise

Willie Wonka is looking for a great new chocolate bar to make in his "Chocolate Factory."

Follow the clues below to create the perfect bar for Willie.

▼ $\frac{1}{6}$ is mint (colour green)
▼ $\frac{1}{4}$ is caramel filled (colour golden brown)
▼ $\frac{1}{12}$ is dark chocolate (colour dark brown)
▼ $\frac{1}{12}$ is white chocolate (colour white)
▼ $\frac{5}{8}$ has rice crisps (colour speckled)

Now, design your own!

Tell a friend about each flavour using fractions.

Is anyone hungry?

Let's make a deal!

Make a deal with someone in your family.

"If you pull a nickel out of this paper bag, I'll do all the dishes. If you pull a penny out, you've got to do them!"

▼ How many of each coin should you put in the bag?
▼ How can you guarantee not having to do the dishes?

Party Time

Imagine you're having a pizza party and 5 kids have been invited over.

▼ You estimate that each kid will eat 3 pieces. (Don't forget yourself!)
▼ If each pizza is cut into 8 pieces, how many whole pizzas will you need to order?

(Use the pizzas below to help you figure it out!)

What fraction will be left over?

Dream Design

Have you always wanted that dream room but never been allowed to design your own? Here's your chance!

The grid below represents your new room. Each square stands for 1 square metre.

What's the **area** of the room? What's the **perimeter**?

6 m

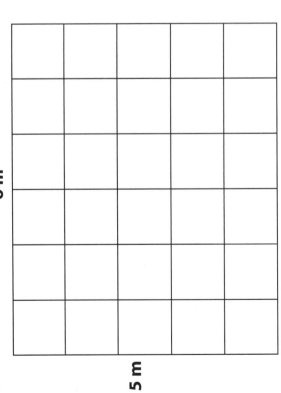

5 m

▲ Draw in furniture where you would like it placed. (Pretend you're looking down from the ceiling.)

▲ Estimate the actual size of real furniture and cover the right number of squares. (A queen-size bed would cover approximately 2 squares by $2\frac{1}{2}$ squares.)

▲ Colour your furniture.

Let's take a closer look …

▲ What area of floor space does your bed take up?

▲ Is it more or less than the dresser?

▲ What's the area of the "empty" floor space?

▲ Find the perimeter of 3 different pieces of furniture.

▲ If your room was only $\frac{1}{2}$ the size, would you still be able to fit all the furniture in? How could you test your prediction?

Great news! Now you get to design your floor!

Use at least 3 different colours to create an interesting tile pattern on the grid below. Think repeating and growing patterns!

6 m

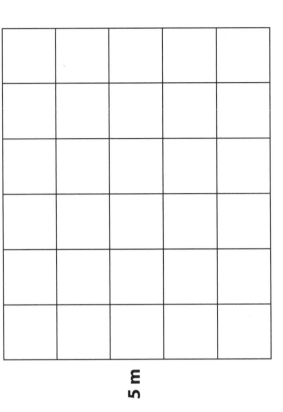

5 m

Show your design to your family. Do you think they'll go for it?

Copyright © 2004 Pearson Education Canada Inc. Not to be copied.